CONFIDENCE

**Transforming your Body to Transform your Mind.
A systematic approach to Unwavering Discipline!**

Frank Cosenza MA CSCS PN1

ISBN: 978-1-64746-649-7 (Paperback)
ISBN: 978-1-64746-650-3 (Hardback)
ISBN: 978-1-64746-651-0 (Ebook)

TABLE OF CONTENTS

FOREWORD

Have you ever felt like you meet trainer after trainer, all who promise to get you into "the best shape of your life?" Have you seen the ad posts on social media trying to sell you the latest gadget that will supposedly help you meet your fitness goals? You get excited. Maybe this time will be different. So, you sign up or purchase yet another fitness tool, only to learn you have fallen prey to the marketing scheme once again. Yeah, I see and hear about this situation often. I have watched people buy one workout program after another and diet after diet plan with no lasting success.

My work as an Olympic-level sports physical therapist often makes me skeptical of trainers and the fitness ruses on the market. In my clinical practice, I have treated patients who have sustained injuries from ill-programmed workouts or the "no pain, no gain" attitude. From my perspective, that mindset is misleading and often deters people from pursuing attainable fitness goals. In my experience, there is only one way to lose weight, keep it off, and gain muscle mass to be "toned" or "ripped." It's daily discipline.

I learned that truth as I worked alongside Olympic athletes. It's all about the day in and day out. Soon after, Frank Cosenza walked into my personal fitness journey. We connected on the idea that effort and dedication are vital to achieving any goal in life. We spoke about the gimmicks many trainers sell and how most people do not realize knowing the basics is key to building strength, endurance, and better health; one must know these basics well and move within them fluidly to gain a solid foundation to excel upon. From our conversation alone, I knew I had met a trainer and strength coach who actually got it.

For many of us, we embark on a fitness journey aiming to improve our health and reach our body goals. A life in good health and mental wellness is important, but I want to go a little deeper because I know well-being starts in the mind. Our ability to better ourselves in any format begins with our inward beliefs. As human beings we all have an innate desire for connection and belonging. We often attach this idea of "belonging" to our appearance, status, or popularity, yet, the key to fulfilling this innate desire is much more simplistic. It is not an outward expression; rather, the key is an inner knowing, a connection to ourselves, a belief system.

You see, if I am going to put in the work and effort to make my fitness goals a reality, I also want whatever I spend my time doing to teach me valuable skills that will transcend into my personal life. I want to get more out of it; I want fitness to benefit my mind also. (I am the ultimate multi-tasker, and I appreciate a good "multi-purpose" item.)

But the question is whether that is even possible. I say it is. Strength training can truly make you a better adjusted human through physical and mental discipline. Wait, what? You don't believe me?

Well, pick up a really heavy weight. Cradle the weight in your hands like a goblet cup close to your chin and perform a squat—five sets of ten repetitions with only a 30-second rest break in between each set, to be exact. Then, tell me if your opinion changes. I bet it does. With this simple exercise, you will get a glimpse of what you are made of. Watch how you respond to the muscle burn, the heavy breathing, and the muscle fatigue. Pay attention to your thought process and where you are mentally. Are you willing to see it through? Or will you stop prematurely because the task is too demanding? Whatever the answer, I promise you one thing: you will meet yourself there, fair and square.

When you train for strength, you cannot hide from "who you are"—your inner world and your connection to self. When you are asked to lift a heavier weight than what you are used to lifting, I guarantee that mental garbage (fears, mental blocks, and self-limiting beliefs) will rise to the forefront of your mind. But as humans we possess a unique gift: we can progress, we can overcome. This is where you keep the commitment to yourself and learn mental fortitude. Strength training teaches this valuable skill. It challenges your mind and your distorted beliefs to restore your focus and the faith in yourself and your capabilities. Now that is what I call a mental health benefit. (See . . . I love a good "multi-purpose" item!)

What I have come to understand is that when you commit to a proper training program and you put the work in—it gives back to you. Breaking mental barriers in the gym gives you the courage to break through mental barriers in your life. That's where the confidence comes from. The breakthroughs harness a growing tenacity from within—a resilience. The outgrowth of self-acceptance, self-reliance, and bravery equals confidence. A belief system. In addition to the body goal you will work hard to attain, these mindful benefits are by-products of strength training as well. This is what strength training did for me; and if you put in the work too, that's what it will do for you. Day in and day out.

As an experienced clinician, I know that every person can improve their quality of life and enhance their functionality if they move more. In this book, Frank Cosenza is willing to breakdown the essence of exercise and unlock the mystery of gaining strength. He dives into foundational exercises and explain how these movements will get you to your fitness and body goals. This book will guide you and provide a straightforward approach to train your body optimally with by-products of mental strength and confidence.

If you want to maximize your training to attain your body goals with a structured approach, then pick up some weights—and this book—because major lessons await.

Frank Cosenza teaches us how to build confidence from the ground up. He keeps it simple.

Thank you, Frank.

Cheers to Our Better Selves,

Dr. Dionne Vernon, PT, DPT, PES, BCS
Movement Specialist, Olympic Sports Physical Therapist
Personal Development Strategist & Speaker
Website: www.dionnevernon.com
IG: @healingcompass

INTRODUCTION

"The idea is that when you start out training slowly
with good form, you allow the entire fabric of all of the
involved systems to engage in the action. This added
dimension of connectivity will then be recruited for
increased force production, stability, and speed."

—*Fascia Training: A Whole-System Approach*
by Bill Parisi and Johnathon Allen[1]

True Confidence is forged through years of effort
and toil. Skipping the work can lead to a false sense
of confidence, which leads to acceptance of the status quo. As a child with limited understanding of
how the world worked, I assumed that after college

I would be handed millions of dollars with little to no effort. Boy, was I naïve! Annoyingly, I am still waiting for the millions to be handed to me. It is safe to say that without effort, energy, and work, you cannot accomplish much. For me, creating confidence has been a lifelong quest. Throughout this process, I have questioned my ability to belong and find a purpose in my life. In this book, I am going to share with you how I inadvertently found all of those things through strength training.

I have been in the fitness industry since 2006, and prior to that I spent my formative years at the gym getting in shape to play sports. I grew up Brooklyn, New York, one of six kids to two full-time working parents. Their schedules were busy, and with a house of eight people, the place was always chaotic. I was searching for my thing, and I found it in sports. Wanting only to play was how it started, but it eventually morphed into something more. I had never really worked out prior to high school sports, and like most young kids, I had no idea what I was doing. I can tell you I was out of shape, overweight, and willing to do what was necessary to play. I continued to show up, no matter how embarrassed I was that I couldn't do a push-up or how sore I became. If I wanted to play football, I had decided that was what I needed to do—keep showing up. Looking back on it, I think that consistency truly helped me understand what it meant to work. The simple thought process helped me to develop my work ethic in the face of exhaustion and fatigue. To this day, I am not always motivated to perform a workout, but I continue to show up!

In the following pages, I hope to share with you my journey on how I created a different existence for myself. Following my story, I will outline my strategies to help you build your own foundation for living a different life. I am writing this book to help everyone achieve more from themselves and their lives. I am going to share with you everything I know about health, wellness, and nutrition to assist you on your own quest to creating more. Everything in these pages is based on my 20 plus years of experience and my education in exercise science. My hope is to demonstrate that there is no magic to it. In fact, you probably already know the formula.

My aim is to help make health and fitness a more important aspect of your life. By caring for your physical well-being, you can improve all aspects of your life. The strategy is simple to follow and will help you reshape how you view, incorporate, and perform physical activity in your life. I have created an easy-to-follow routine you can adapt to your lifestyle, whether you are just starting out or have years under your belt lifting weights. I will shed light on how simple this process should be to help you reap the many benefits once we create the necessary habits required.

Through my many years of working out, I have been reminded several times just how much lifting weights and life seem to mirror one another. There is no better metaphor for life than lifting weights.

When everything seems to be going against you, whether in life or in the gym; you simply need to stand up. Working out gave me the confidence to attack many obstacles in life and not to be afraid to take risks. I have in some capacity attacked my life as I would any workout—head on, with little to no regard for my body.

This book begins with my teenage years, high school, where, like many people, I was searching to find a way to express myself. I found my voice through sports and lifting weights. I was a short, unfit, unathletic teenager who should never have been allowed to be on the field, but I was determined to play. All of that was made possible through my efforts in the gym, where I constantly pushed my limits and my physical ability. Every day I showed up and put in the work to transform myself in the hopes of getting playing time. I have not looked back or stopped since, and at the age of 37, my journey continues. I have come to understand a lot about myself over the years, and I have realized just how much physical activity and being physically fit has prepared me for life.

In the second part of the book, I will help you create your own confidence with a simple to follow outline of my thought-process. The premise of this thought-process is to undo all the damage from the myths the fitness industry has told you over the years. I have become utterly disgusted with the state of affairs in health and fitness. Nowadays, everywhere you look on the internet is another advertisement for weight loss supplements, a program to get "shredded" in three days, or the latest piece of equipment to give you "the body of your dreams." It drives me crazy every time I see one of these ridiculous claims. Look, I understand health and fitness is a multi-billion dollar a year industry. Every day, millions of dollars are being spent to try to expedite the process of weight loss or muscle gain. Entrepreneurs and companies alike are trying to revolutionize the tried and true techniques for achieving the perfect body, whatever that may be. Don't believe the hype!

Working out is a necessity for countless reasons. Primarily, though, it is necessary to combat how our society has become all about convenience. Literally everything is at the swipe of a screen. Our jobs are no longer building the infrastructure and great cities we live in. Most of us are no longer farming crops or butchering our animals for food. In fact, most people don't even take trips to the grocery store anymore, because they can now have it delivered. We are all trying to scratch out a living in this world and working crazy schedules to accommodate the fast-paced reality we now live in, but we have begun sacrificing our health in service of it. I am here to help you take back your health and, hopefully, simplify the process for you.

The philosophy behind the strategy is simplicity. I want to give you your life back to share with your loved ones by going out and creating memories through new experiences. The objective is to cut down the time you spend in the gym in order to maximize your life outside of it. By focusing on five foundational exercises, you will no longer have to perform thirty movements in the gym. My hope is that with the principles laid out, you won't even perform five movements in the gym per workout. The foundational exercises are comprised of compound movements or multi-joint exercises that incorporate several muscle groups. The benefit to using these movements can be applied to just about any goal. Whether it is weight loss or strength gains, these exercises are the basis for just about every other movement in the gym—or life, for that matter. Again, the purpose here is not to turn you into a powerlifter; it is to help get you moving optimally for your performance called *life*.

The foundational exercises that will be explained in detail are as follows: the squat, the deadlift, the overhead press, the pull-up, and the bench press. Perfecting these exercises will be the basis for your new workout regimen. These exercises focus on force production, energy expenditure, and proper movement mechanics that will translate into your daily life. Each exercise selected, if performed properly, can propel your physical and mental ability to new heights. The combination of these five exercises will instill a confidence in you to tackle any obstacles you face. The ability to perform these exercises well will also create a strong foundation that can be applied to any athletic pursuit. These movements are the core fundamentals for just about every training technique across the board. Their applications, when mastered, are endless. They are the principles of elite training performance programs world-wide. I will break down and explain each movement for you to implement safely and effectively—into your daily workout.

Once we have a master training plan, we can begin to discuss eating habits or diet. No longer will you look at the word "diet" as a list of things you can't eat. Hopefully, when all is said and done, you will look at the word "diet" and think "fuel." There is a plethora of information available, but again, the objective here is to simplify it and give you only the foundations of how to fuel your body properly to perform optimally. Eating habits are traditionally hard to break due to our emotional attachments to food. However, if I can get you to look at your food as fuel for your day and performance, then we can start to create change. The guidelines and strategy will be simple enough for you to incorporate in your day without having to break the bank on organic, non-GMO, gluten-free, fat-free, grain-free, dairy-free, or meat-free foods. I want to teach you how to fuel your body for your lifestyle. How you choose to implement the rules will be up to you!

The formula is not a flashy incantation that you will need to practice for several years to master. At its core, it is about simplicity and erasing all the myths from your mind regarding what healthy is supposed to be. The strategy is consistent work for a period to achieve the results you are after, or simply put:

I am not trying to sell you any gimmicks or gadgets to achieve results. I am insisting that you understand this journey will take work. Come prepared every day to work your hardest, stick to the guidelines for your eating habits, and you will see results. I cannot tell you how long it will take or that your expected results will look like mine, because you aren't me. You have your own life, stressors, and issues you deal with that I know nothing about. This isn't a "get ripped quick" or "drop 100 pounds tomorrow" book. This book is the actual script to understanding how to implement and create a proper workout routine to regain your confidence in life. This book will teach you basic fundamentals that, if you apply them, should exceed your expectations, but it is based on you and your work. I cannot do the work for you, I cannot meal prep for you, and I certainly cannot eat for you. To have the life you want and the body you need to make it happen is based solely on your ownership of this routine. If you can master the basics that I map out in the pages to come, you will be able to conquer anything. That is the one guarantee I can give you!

MY STORY

Each player must accept the cards life deals them,
but once they are in hand, you alone must decide how to
play the cards in order to win the game.

—Voltaire[2]

know what you're thinking. "Why should I listen
to some guy who has worked out for 20 years?
Furthermore, you own a gym, so of course you
are going to try to sell me on being in shape and
getting stronger."

While I have spent more of my life inside the
gym than outside of it (and yes, I own a gym), the
purpose of this book is to help you feel the same

level of confidence I have every day, to help you reach a potential that has escaped you for too long. I want to share with you my story of failures in order to help you learn from my mistakes. The reason I believe I am qualified to share this strategy with you is because it has taken me failing in the gym for more than half my life to understand what I should have been doing this whole time, in and out of the gym. The story of simplicity and mastery are one and the same, and hopefully by the end of my story you will understand two things: how I have come to this conclusion and how it can benefit you.

My story really begins in high school, where, like most other adolescents, I was trying to find my thing; I was also trying to find my thing at home to stand out from my siblings. I am lucky number five out of six kids. My siblings seemingly all had their thing going on and I still didn't have mine. My oldest sister is ten years my senior; Christina is the firstborn and paved the way for the rest of us. Melissa, the second oldest (six years older than me), is the bookworm and completely different from Christina in many ways. In fact, she is different from most people I know. She enjoyed school so much she stayed there as long as possible, earning a Ph.D. in biology and eventually a Doctor of Veterinary Science degree in 2012. John, my older brother (four years older than me), is the first son, named after my father and his father. He is artistic and can draw anything. He also taught himself guitar, and in high school, he got into photography. He is someone I have always looked up to and wanted to be like but never had a chance, I can't draw a stick figure straight. Lisa (three years older than me), the youngest girl, was a cheerleader, Daddy's little girl, and a straight-A student. She is just seemingly well-rounded and a cross between Chris the social butterfly and Melissa the nerd, only seemingly more popular; we got a lot closer later in life. Then there was me, Frank (middle son), a pudgy kid, really nothing interesting about me yet. Finally, Joseph or Joey (four years younger than me) is the baby. He is a mixture of all of us since he basically had seven parents growing up. He is a good athlete (better than me), he loves music, enjoys cooking, is super loud and funny, and seemingly is a jack of all trades. As the baby, he pretty much got away with everything. He once blew up a toilet with some smuggled firecrackers on a school trip and barely got in trouble; he maybe got grounded for three days, if that.

High school was where I finally found my niche via sports. As I mentioned, I was a pudgy kid—polite way of saying fat. Grandma Pedone use to call me "chunky."

(10/11 years old, 1993-1994,
one of my sisters' sweet 16 parties)

As a freshman in high school, I weighed 185 pounds and stood 5'3". So, here I was, a short, fat, little kid, deciding I was going to go out for my high school football team. Having never played organized football—or any contact sport for that matter, I am not sure what I thought I was doing. I can honestly say I don't remember what made me think I could do it, but I showed up anyway. I walked up to the coach, introduced myself, and said I wanted to play the next season. Then I asked him what I would have to do. He explained that I would need to come to workouts every day after school, show up for summer conditioning before camp, make it through camp, and then try out for the team. My school didn't cut anyone really, so I did exactly what the coach said.

I showed up to work out the very next day. It was my first for many things: working out and changing in front of people who weren't family. I decided that to save time and to save myself the embarrassment of getting undressed in front of strangers, I would layer my gym clothes under my school clothes. I thought it was completely normal and didn't second-guess myself. Class let out, and I made my way to the gymnasium where the weight room was located in the corner. It wasn't big by any standards. There wasn't a ton of equipment in there, but it was my second home for the next four years. After stripping down to my gym shorts and t-shirt, I was ready to begin.

There was only one problem. I had no idea what the hell I was doing. I sat down on a chair thing, which was the only thing not being used. It had what I thought a foot rest until my coach said, "Don't just sit there. Press it!"

So, I did, not really counting the repetitions (reps) or acknowledging the weight. I did as I was told. I didn't know any better. At the end of the time, I looked at the weight. It was 300 pounds. Man, I am strong, I thought. First day, and I already pressed 300 pounds with my legs. That has got to be some kind of record. It wasn't!

The piece of equipment was called a universal machine, combining several pieces of equipment in one massive metal structure. It had a dip station, pull-down station, chest press, pull-up bar, and a low cable curl attachment. I was beaming with confidence, and then I saw something amazing. A teammate was doing dips. He moved so effortlessly and smoothly. He looked like he was floating, yet he was moving so quickly and hammering them out countlessly. Surely with my new amazing strength I could do those. I had just leg pressed 300 pounds; this would be a piece of cake! At the end of his set, as everyone was heading out, I jumped up to demonstrate my awesomeness. I was prepared to obliterate some reps. Wrong! The only thing that was obliterated was my ego. I jumped up to perform a dip and immediately and epically failed, straight down. I don't even think I slowed myself that first time. How is this possible? I thought. I was beside myself. Apparently doing leg presses on a universal machine does nothing for your upper body. Who knew? That settled it. Every day after my workout I would attempt a dip, no matter what.

So, I did. Monday through Friday from 4-4:45 p.m., once I was done working out, I would attempt a single dip. Every day, without exception, I would fail to perform one. At best, I was beginning to slow my descent, but I still hadn't accomplished a dip. After three months or so of failing miserably to perform a dip, I told myself I would need to get more serious. I decided I would perform sit-ups and push-ups in my room every night before I showered. I started with trying to perform ten reps of each, eventually working up to 40 reps of each or four rounds of ten reps. I would alternate to give myself rest. I hooked my feet under my dresser and got to work. I knew a push-up test was coming for summer camp, and I didn't want to fail, so I tried to get to at least 50 by summer's end. It would be close, especially since I wasn't really able to perform them straight yet.

That summer, John was working at GNC and brought home the most amazing book, with one of my favorite actors on the cover—Arnold Schwarzenegger. Apparently, he had an entire encyclopedia on how to work out. I thought, *This guy is huge. He has to know what he's talking about.* Initially, I would steal the book from my brother and look through it, staring at the amazing physiques those guys had—guys like Sergio Oliva, Frank Columbo, Lou Ferrigno, and Lee Priest. Holy cow, I have to follow what these guys say. Just look at them, I thought to myself. I read all about the different exercises and training styles they performed. John finally bequeathed me the book, begrudgingly, I imagine.

That book would change my life. The first thing it taught me was that you can train abdominals (abs) and calf muscles every day, and the best abdominal exercise wasn't a sit-up but a crunch, so I got rid of the sit-ups and starting pumping out crunches. The guys in that book had abs for days; of course I was going to listen to them. Needless to say, it wouldn't be until much later I would learn about steroids and their usage, but, at the time I was happily ignorant.

I followed my plan until camp finally came around. I tried out for the team, still embarrassed to change or sweat in front of the team. I still layered my clothing. We performed our testing. Unfortunately, it was a running test, and my fat little body hated running. I didn't do well. However, the coaches seemed to take it easy on the new recruits and told us we didn't need to pass it that time. I went to camp with the team and made junior varsity (JV) as a backup center and outside linebacker.

I enjoyed camp. We got to sleep in cabins in the woods and have ice-cream sandwiches for lunch and dinner. We got to scrimmage other teams that were there as well. It was hard, but I really liked it. The season came, and every day I showed up after school for practice. Then, I would go home, eat, and do my homework. Games were on Sundays. After watching the varsity team play Saturday mornings, I would go home and soak in the bathtub and watch college football because my coaches said that was the best way to learn football, I figured I should follow and support a team. I only had a small black and white TV that didn't get many stations, but it got Fox and NBC. Fox played some Big Ten team usually: Penn State, Ohio State, Purdue, or Wisconsin, but it didn't seem to play the same team regularly. On the other hand, NBC always played Notre Dame, the team with gold helmets. I remember seeing those helmets and being in awe; I settled on Notre Dame to follow as my favorite team.

(1999, sophomore year, high school)

As the season wound down late in October, something happened that would propel my fitness journey to a new level. I was coming home on the bus one evening after practice, and as I stepped off the bus to walk around the corner to my house, my pants and shorts all fell down to my ankles. I was in shock! Thankfully, I am short and wore oversized shirts, so no one had to see my little boy package. I scooped up my pants and darted home as quickly as I could. I ran upstairs to the bathroom, stripped down, and hopped on the scale. I can still remember the feeling of seeing that number, 140 pounds. That can't be right, I thought, so I checked the scale to make sure it was zeroed out and stepped back on; 140 pounds, again. What the? I had lost 45 pounds and hadn't noticed at all! Since I was still layering my clothes, I prevented myself and most others from ever noticing that my body had changed. *Holy cow, now I will need to work out or I will die*, I thought. *How am I gonna survive if I don't?*

Fortunately, my parents recognized I was going to continue to play football, so they got me a bench set for Christmas. I would use almost every day after school to try to bulk up; I wanted to get ripped eventually, because that's how it works right? Little did I know! I taped my summer workouts up on the bookshelf and spent the summer working out in the basement that year. Oh, the joys of being a teen and having summers off from school! Except, Mom and Dad said I needed to get a job if I wanted to continue to play because they weren't paying for me to go to camp. *That's not fair*, I thought. *None of my friends have to pay, why should I?* I was not happy, but when I was sixteen I had to get a summer job mowing lawns to pay for camp. Lesson number one from Mom and Dad about work: If you want to do something, you'd better be willing to work for it. I'm so grateful for that valuable lesson, although I am sure at the time I was very unappreciative of it. Every day in the summer from then on, the routine was mowing lawns and working out.

High school went like that for the next three years. I got very serious about my workouts and spent a majority of my time in preparation for football. If I wasn't in a gym somewhere, you could catch me running from my house on 31st in Brooklyn to Marine Park, making my way around the track and then back home. I was determined to become a better player by becoming stronger. Since I wasn't a stellar runner, I spent a lot of time working on that skill. In fact, my junior year, my coaches made me join the track team. My role on the track team was distance—keep running around the track until practice was over. School at that time was merely time between training sessions. My parents would never accept failing grades, since they were both teachers, and I could never allow my grades to jeopardize football, so I did what was expected of me in the classroom. I got good grades and so I didn't spend too much time worrying about school work. I carried a fairly high-B to low-A average across the board.

I had no clue what I was going to do after high school. I was enrolled in James Madison High School in the law program. I took and passed the curriculum as I was expected to, yet none of that seemed to matter because my mind was only worried about my workouts for football. I showed up every day, did the homework, took the tests, but did I retain anything? Probably not; I merely got through it with no issues. Getting an education wasn't really challenging until graduate school. In both high school and college, all I cared about was football, my workouts for football, and getting playing time.

I graduated, passing all my tests and curriculum easily. Now, it was off to college, but was I ready to go to? Absolutely not! However, to please my parents I went, following the same path as in high school, enrolling in the criminal justice program at Utica College of Syracuse University. I selected the school because they were going to let me play football, but truth be told I still don't think I should have gone to college yet. I didn't really know what I wanted to do, but if I had to go to school, I was going to play football. College football and high school football are two totally different beasts. College programs are faster, more demanding (it's practically a full-time job), and require way more time in meetings. Like high school, though, it was a challenge, and I craved it. The competitive nature, the camaraderie, the struggle, and the pain were all something I needed to get through the drudgery of classes. Once again, classes were merely a pause between lifting and playing football.

College course work was nothing compared to the mental and physical preparation for football. I couldn't tell you anything of any importance I did inside the classroom, but I could tell you all the different work I had to put into playing football on that level. It was grueling, miserable, and painful, and I loved it. It probably broke me mentally a handful of times but like an addict I continued to come back for more. My freshman year I made special teams, abusing my body to run down field on punt and kick-off coverage for the chance to make a tackle or have an impact on the game. It was a thrill to travel with the team all over the country to play, but I craved a larger role and knew I would have to work extra hard going in to the next season if I wanted to make an impact. So, I took my workouts and knowledge, and over the summer, I kicked my butt getting ready for my chance.

I decided my sophomore year would be different. I knew what to expect and went to camp in the best shape of my life having run and practiced all summer long to prepare. Being undersized and having a huge chip on my shoulder would eventually catch up to me that season. I sustained two injuries requiring surgery early in the season. I would forfeit my sophomore year and take medical red-shirt to recover and not be penalized a year of eligibility, which is a big deal when you only have four years for your college career. I would love to say those were the only injuries I sustained and that I would go on to have a tremendously productive junior and senior season, but unfortunately, it seemed to be only the beginning of what was to come. I had three injuries that year: torn meniscus (cartilage) in my left knee, torn labrum (cartilage) in my left shoulder, and destroyed tendons and ligaments in my thumb, which is still deformed because I never got it fixed. It was a season I would love to forget, but looking back, it helped me learn so much. All I cared about was getting back in the gym after each surgery. My thought process was that I could still work with the body parts that weren't damaged, and I could get a jump on preparation for off-season conditioning. At the time, it made sense.

Unfortunately, as summer rolled around, I got a weird cold that simply wouldn't go way. School let out in May, and by the time I could see a doctor, I was back in Brooklyn working and trying to get through my workouts. I remember warming up with a weight on the bench and it feeling incredibly heavy. My throat was super sore, and it felt like I was swallowing knives every time I tried to drink or eat anything. I finally confided in my parents, and they sent me to the doctor. The doctor drew blood, but while we waited for my blood work, my doctor suggested I see a specialist (ear, nose and throat). I went to the specialist and waited longer in the waiting room than I spent with the doctor. He literally peered into my throat, proclaimed that I was contagious and needed to be escorted out and shouldn't touch anything. They made me stand in the hallway waiting for the nurse to give me the prescription.

By the time I got home, the news from the blood work was back: I had mononucleosis! I knew this was going to inhibit my summer conditioning. I was quarantined to my room for the next four weeks, finally coming out by my birthday, June 17. We reported for camp on August 15, so that gave me about two months to work. I had to choose weights or running to maximize my training time. I chose weights to build my strength back up, having shrunk down to 160-165 pounds. I needed to get back to my playing weight of 180-185 pounds or there would be no playing time for me. Man, that was a tough training summer. Running was brutal, and training seemed to be crushing, but I got through it once again, kicking my own butt. I followed most of the summer workouts minus the majority of the running. I still practiced my 300-yard shuttle runs between manhole covers. I would go in front of my house in the middle of the street every night; I needed to pass that running test.

When the two months were up, I reported to camp. Lifting went well, but I failed my running test, and was forced to go to remedial running. That was a sign of things to come in my junior season.

While playing in a scrimmage game, someone fell on my ankle. Fearing it was broken, they took me off the field on a cart. X-rays would have to wait since my foot swelled up like a balloon. When I was finally able to get x-rays, it turned out I didn't break my ankle. As soon as the swelling subsided enough to get my cleats on, I tried to get back on the field. Having missed the season prior, I was anxious to play. However, in my haste, I didn't let my ankle heal, and that only increased the damage done, which eventually led to the end of my football career. That time I needed not one, but two surgeries, to fix the damage. The first surgery took place in August that summer, but when I was in physical therapy, I couldn't perform the simplest warm-up exercises, so they had me perform pool workouts for six weeks.

After getting back to dry land work, I again failed remedial exercises, falling over when asked to perform a wall squat, so my physical therapists insisted I get a second opinion from an ankle specialist. The second surgery would officially end my career, as it was a total reconstruction of my ankle—two finger-length screws and two plates placed into my ankle to hold it together. When I was out of surgery, the doctor, said they couldn't recommend I play again, That didn't stop me, however. The very next day I was in the gym, thinking the doctors had no idea what they were talking about. I had one good leg and upper body work to do, so I did. The recovery process seemed endless, lasting well into the second semester of my senior year, so I couldn't play any longer. I would say it broke my heart, but it was a blessing in disguise. I had spent too much of my time thinking I could play forever, never seeing that I had to finish school. Graduation was looming and real life was coming. Finishing college was easy enough; it was figuring out the next steps that would be a considerably harder challenge.

I indeed graduated college, but like most people who were unaware of what they wanted when they began school, I was still very much lost. I continued to pursue the path I was set on, which was law school, but deep down, I knew it just wasn't the life for me. I never really loved it like I did football; it never felt like a challenge. The legal profession was by no means easy, but it was extremely monotonous and lackluster. After graduation, I worked in a handful of different law firms as a legal secretary, but I never loved it. I continued to work out because I feared getting fat and going back to my pre-football self. I was very conscious of what I was eating at the time, but I didn't say no to cake, cookies or anything sweet, and I definitely enjoyed drinking on the weekends. Ultimately, I didn't see myself following through with law school, which was confirmed when I got my law school admission test score, a very average 147. No law school was taking me with that score! Suddenly, I was out of college with no plan for a career, having botched my law school admissions test.

For the next six months, I worked at Michael's catering hall, as I had done since my senior year in high school and throughout college, where my brother Joe and best friend Matt were still working. Every day was the same: wake up, go lift, shower, and then go to Michael's to work. Most of my time would be spent horsing around with my friends at work. Rinse, lather, and repeat. I hated this part of my life. I had zero direction and no clue what I was doing, so the gym was my only escape. I never missed a session and made sure I worked as hard as I could. Eventually, the guys at Michael's started asking to join my workouts, and I obliged them, as they merely mirrored what I did. I didn't know how to train people; I just liked working out and loved having new partners try to keep up. My brother Joe was the only person who ever could. If it wasn't for my brother pushing me and purchasing my certifications over the next few months, I probably would have stayed at Michael's for way too long and never gotten out of my parents' house. For the second time in my life, my family intervened, demonstrating a plan unknown to me. Joe saw how I was when I was in the gym and helped me get my first training certification. I have never really thanked him or my brother John, so here, in this book I will. Thank you both from the bottom of my heart for having such a positive impact on me and helping me figure things out, even when I didn't know what I was doing. Each of my siblings has helped me through many obstacles, and for that I will always be indebted to them.

I immediately started doing the work for my certification in personal training. I began to read and dive into the subjects of kinesiology, anatomy, and physiology. I knew I didn't know anything about the human body, and my reading showed me that. I also knew I couldn't get enough of the stuff. It was so interesting learning the different mechanisms that work to make the body perform. I was literally in heaven learning all the material, and all of the exercises I had been doing over the years were starting to come alive. Learning about the joints and the prime muscle movers that make the action happen was stimulating my mind. It was incredible. There was nothing dull or boring about the information. The only issue was I couldn't get enough, and I was eager to understand more and more. That was early 2006. I was a year removed from college, and for the first time there was hope I was heading in a positive direction. I was finally excited about something, and I wanted to try to absorb as much as I could.

I would eventually get hired by a huge corporate gym at an entry-level personal trainer position. The company had a mandatory education system which fed my hunger for knowledge. The training put me back into a classroom setting, only this time I was soaking up the information, trying to suck up every ounce. If there was something offered I didn't know, I jumped at the chance, sitting in on every workshop or in-house education class I could. I wanted to know everything. I felt I was behind the eight ball because I did not have a traditional background or real education within the field of exercise science. I didn't want to fail at this because I loved working out. It had done so much for me— from losing weight to setting records in the weight room. I wanted to help others experience that. I was determined to make it work.

It was around that time I knew I had found my calling, and that I would eventually go back to graduate school for this subject. I wasn't sure where, and I wasn't sure when, but I had discussed it openly with my dad. I would spend the next six years working with that company, moving up through the ranks, becoming the highest level trainer within six months. That didn't seem to satiate my hunger for knowledge, so I turned next to management, which seemed fitting. I liked being in charge and always liked taking the lead. It was a natural progression, but I was far too young and too immature to make the best of it. I did one thing in my time as a manager that was good and that was hire and befriend Joe Gernetzke, my eventual business partner.

Joe and I would become inseparable over the next year of my life. We had similar upbringings, we shared the same viewpoints when it came to training our clients, and we were the same age. We would go on to have a memorable 2008 running around the city that never sleeps. He also shared my vision to go back to graduate school and start a personal training company. We spent 2008 conspiring and planning to find graduate programs and begin the process of launching our own gym where we would be the ones to decide how it was run. We would create and implement the programs and how our clients' results would take shape. That year was definitely a huge turning point and an incredibly memorable year for me.

There were many highs for me and my family. Two of my siblings would get married that year; my first niece, Antonette, would also be born. I was actually named her godfather! In 2008, there was a huge blow to our family as well; my dad was diagnosed with cancer. I am not sure when my parents found out exactly, but they told us kids around Thanksgiving. It was just after my brother's wedding in October. My dad's smoker's cough, which he seemingly had always had, got worse. He and my mom kept the diagnosis from us. I found out from my mother one night after dinner. As she was doing the dishes, she said it matter-of-factly, like she would say anything else. I remember feeling numb, but I don't think the reality of it hit me for quite some time. At 25, I was mature enough to grasp what was said, but I was too stubborn to believe it. I can say now that the news definitely rocked my world and changed everything for me. My dad had just retired. He was just about to get to the good stuff in life—having grandkids, traveling everywhere with my mom. I was angry. I remember thinking, Wait a second, I'm still not married, and I am next in line. He is supposed to be here for me. I need him to tell me how to live. I never expected to lose my dad by 25, but unfortunately, treatment didn't work, and he passed the following April.

I returned to work because I was stubborn and didn't want to accept what had just happened, but I had also declared I wouldn't let what happened to my dad happen to me, so I immediately set my graduate school and gym plan into motion with Joe G. I was leaving New York and going to the University of Texas in Austin to get my master's degree. My father's passing was a catalyst for some serious change. Unfortunately, being a city slicker in Texas didn't work for me. Three months later, I was back in the corporate gym, trying once again to recalibrate and sort out where I could attend graduate school back in New York. A year would pass before I applied and got accepted to Columbia University. That's right, I was now voluntarily going back to school.

While I was in the middle of my application process, during a break between clients at work, some friends and I decided to go play some basket-ball in the park. Remember that ankle injury I had? I was supposed to wear a brace for any sport-like activity, except this was an impromptu decision, and I didn't have my brace with me. I would take it easy, so I figured what was the worst that could happen? Well, five minutes into shooting baskets while wait-ing for all the people to show up, I ran to retrieve a loose ball bouncing its way into another game. I jumped up about two inches from the ground, and my ankle gave way. I heard a very audible pop and immediately thought, Holy shit! I think I just broke my ankle. I waited for the game to be over and tried to walk. I couldn't, so my friend suggested we hop in a cab and go to a nearby hospital. I told him it was probably just a sprain. I hoped I was right.

(2010, Preparation for bodybuilding show
just before breaking my foot)

I ended up shattering my fifth metatarsal, and it would require another surgery to repair the damage. The surgery required a plate the length of my foot and two rivets to hold it in place. My right foot is now bionic, with three plates and four screws holding it together. The x-ray is something to see. For the fourth time, I had to recover from being cut open, and it was the eighth time I had to recover from being put under anesthesia for physical damage to my body from sports. In late 2005, I was in a car accident that had required three treatments under anesthesia to manipulate and put back my surgically repaired left shoulder to neutral anatomical position. Each time afterward, within a week of surgery, I was back working out. This time, I could not follow the same pattern.

Prior to breaking my foot, I was getting ready to compete in my first bodybuilding show, but now that would have to wait. Breaking my foot had me laid up for a month because every time I stood up, the blood would rush to my foot, and I would get light-headed. Fortunately, my sister Melissa and her husband Kessar lived three blocks away from me at the time. Since I lived in a three-story walk-up and couldn't get up the stairs because it would take me ages, and coming back down wouldn't happen, they let me live on their couch. Another obstacle and another sibling to the rescue! Breaking my foot was definitely not in the game plan, but it was another injury to add to my impressive medical dossier and time spent rehabbing with a physical therapist, which meant more ways to learn how to handle and treat people with foot injuries. Firsthand knowledge can't be beat, right? My foot would be fine by the time I actually had to go to classes at Columbia, although I did have to interview with crutches and a boot during the application process. They probably felt sorry for me. I was fine by the time classes came around in September: Sweet victory!

Graduate school was an extremely challenging, due to time management and the course load. I wanted to get my course work over with as quickly as I could, so I took as many classes as possible, along with working a full-time job. It seemed like a sane thing to do. I didn't sleep much that first semester.

During that time, another trainer at work introduced me to her client, Gerwin, who was at Columbia, as well. He looked me over and said, "Hey man, do you play rugby?"

I didn't and told him so. He replied, "Would you want to?"

I immediately said yes and decided to join the business school team at Columbia. My competitive outlet found me, and I wasn't even looking; I immediately knew I needed to play, regardless of what my family and body said to me. No injuries requiring surgery occurred during the two seasons I played. I did, however, dislocate my nose and have a handful of minor bloody cuts, but rugby is awesome, and chicks dig scars, right?

(Photo courtesy of Gerwin Baek, 2010/2011)

By the end of 2010, I was in graduate school, my training business was doing well, and I had met a girl at work. Things were finally going well for me. In fact, another client at the time introduced me to her daughter's friend who was a professional snowboarder. She was in town and needed to train, so she would come to the gym when my client was there. I saw her performing an exercise improperly, and although I was not training her at this time, I went over and adjusted her. I fixed what she was doing and explained why she needed to perform the exercise another way, then showed her how, and off she went. Later that day, I got a message from my client that the snowboarder wanted to train with me. I was ecstatic because it meant I could work with another athlete, and it was exactly what I wanted to be doing—training athletes. My then-girlfriend was training for a bodybuilding show as well, so I was really starting to find my groove. It was pretty cool to have the opportunity to work with such diverse individuals. My regular clients each had a variety of different issues like nerve problems, weight loss, strength, and post-surgical after brain tumor removal—not your typical clientele. It was an incredible learning experience!

At about the same time, the snowboarder wanted me to train her to get her back to full strength; she had just had a surgery six months prior. She had suffered a bad knee injury, and after the surgery she had developed a bone bruise. She explained that she needed to strength train to get back on Team USA. By the end of my first semester, I was on a plane to Colorado to finish my first semester and the remainder of the year training, Brooke Shaw and her siblings, Spencer, Serena, and Maverick. I was there to focus on Brooke, getting her to full strength, but I ended up working with all the kids. My role was to teach them strength training for their snowboarding disciplines. It was an incredible opportunity and I had to go. The semester was coming to a close and I was able to finish all my courses and take all my finals remotely.

It wasn't until second semester, in 2011, that I would hit another obstacle and where a sibling would prove to be invaluable at getting me out of trouble. It turns out graduate school, plus working full-time and playing rugby for fun isn't the proper recipe for health or sleeping. I apparently was spreading myself far too thin. I stayed up late to get through my course work, as I had to work early and then go to class. I was also still avoiding dealing with my father's death, so I'd use school-work or work as an excuse to burn the midnight oil. Well, it eventually destroyed my stomach and forced me to seek medical and psychiatric help to address the issue. The issue in question was not being able to keep anything down that I ate. For an entire month, around March/April I became violently ill and would expel whatever I ate. That forced me to miss more than three weeks of classes and made me rethink my approach to working full-time, carrying a full course load, and playing competitive sports. I eventually got it right and figured out that I would need take fewer credit hours, slowing down my studies to make sure I was able to pass, but I like to learn the hard way. I would have to make up my class work through additional classes the following year, extending my stay at Columbia but teaching me a valuable lesson, one would think.

Things were clicking, and I was humming along, or so I thought. Things were about to get real serious real quick the following semester. In my behavioral human development class, we were tasked to write a research paper on a medical issue of our choosing that could potentially be helped with exercise intervention. I chose to research and write about Parkinson's disease, which my uncle Vinny had. My professor was eager to read my paper because that was her field of expertise. My goal was to demonstrate how exercise intervention as a portion of treatment could possibly alleviate symptoms of Parkinson's disease, most specifically the tremors. During my research, I found out how Tai Chi is used to help diminish the effects of tremors and how people were beginning to explore exercise as a possible solutions for tremors. Unfortunately, while writing the paper I had created a file of all the quotes and material I would be citing and using to make my argument in the paper. I was typing, then copying and pasting from one document into another. I am not sure how it happened, but I inadvertently handed in a plagiarized paper due to really poorly cited and misused quotes. This almost got me expelled. I was given an F (first F ever, mind you), and my case had to go before a review board. They would decide if I was allowed to continue, or if I would be terminated from the program. I was extremely scared that, for the second time in my life, I had failed and would have no direction. Fortunately, someone was looking out for me, because the review board agreed to allow me to finish and get my degree. From that point on, however, I had to make sure my papers were above reproach and properly cited. I once again turned to a sibling. This time it was Lisa. She was always good at school, and we had grown close since high school. Since I was Antonette's godfather, we spoke regularly. My sister would be my saving grace, and she definitely deserves credit for helping me get through graduate school. She still proofreads most of what I write even now. She is someone I have learned to trust and confide in. I may not always agree with her advice, but she always tells me like it is without sugarcoating it. I am and will always be grateful to have her looking out for me.

Graduate school would eventually end for me, once I made up all my required courses and completed the curriculum. There was only one thing standing in my way—either a research paper or a cumulative test. Being that I had such an issue with writing papers, I felt it was wiser to take the test. I would have to wait for them to run the test, and that wouldn't happen until October 2012. I had completed my courses and was happy to wait for the opportunity to be able to take the final. I did pass the test without any issues, and in October of 2012, I received my Master's in Applied Physiology. During my down time between classes finishing and the examination, I had reached out to Joe G. to discuss once again the plan that was set in motion in 2008. I was direct and to the point with Joe G. I was ready to leave New York and wanted to make the move to start the business we had discussed. He was still in Texas at the time and had decided he was prepared to make a move as well. Given that New York was out as a desired end location and Texas was out for me, we decided to meet in the middle where Joe had grown up and his family still lived—Columbus, Ohio. On November 1, 2012, I packed my things in a U-Haul and for the second time, left New York to try to make my mark in the fitness industry. We were going to open our gym under the name of Sentinel Performance.

From November to January, I interviewed and tried to get a job with any gym willing to hire me in Columbus, Ohio. I didn't want to be a trainer again, so I applied for management positions, figuring I could capitalize on my experience from the years prior. I truly didn't want a job doing it again, but I needed the money. Once again, as luck would have it, I found myself linked up with a team. This time it was Olympic lifting, a sport and style of training I fell in love with when I was 25, right around the time my dad was diagnosed with cancer. In fact, I loved it so much I competed in it several times, winning in 2008 and 2010. For those who don't know, weightlifting is indeed an Olympic sport. This sport requires participants to compete at lifting in two disciplines, the snatch and the clean and jerk. The goal is to lift as much weight in each discipline as possible; a lifter is allowed only three attempts. The snatch goes first. This movement is extremely complicated and the objective is to move a weight from the floor to an overheard position in one motion. The clean and jerk, while ending in a similar position, has a different path. During the "clean" part (usually the heavier of the two lifts), the weight is lifted from the floor to the shoulder position during the catch (front rack) before the lifter stands up and then jerks—a transition from shoulder to overhead catch position. The "jerk" is the name of the way a lifter drops under and extends the weight up before standing up with weight overhead. There are two variations—either a split stance jerk or a squat jerk, but both finish the same way. The picture below shows the front rack position of my clean before I attempt the jerk.

When I heard there was a team in Columbus, I sought them out and joined, training under Olympic coach Mark Cannella, or Bubbi as I affectionately called him. He was like the old Jewish mother to all the lifters, constantly worrying about something each one of us had to do. It was a fun time. I would go on to compete with the team four or five times.

(2014 Meet in Ohio. Mark Cannella is looking on in black t-shirt, head tilted.)

In January 2014, I competed in Pittsburgh with the team. It was maybe my second competition with the team. As usual, I did my thing to lift at 77 kg weight-class, a weight class lower than my normal day to day bodyweight. . Mark was against cutting to go down in weight-class, but that's where I felt comfortable and had competed prior, winning both times, so he let me go ahead. There was nothing special about the meet. Everything was going according to plan. Weigh-in was fine, warm-ups were fine, my snatches went great, and now it was time for the clean and jerk portion. Again, warm-ups went smoothly. I made my opener at 110 kg, then my second at 115 kg. My next and final attempt was at 120 kg. I had not hit this weight in Columbus yet and was eager to make the lift. I still have the video and it's extremely hard to see, but I would in fact get injured once again during sports. The clean portion went up with no real problem; then it was time to jerk the weight overhead. I jumped under the bar, locking it out overhead. The weight rocked my shoulder in the socket a bit, and I felt a sting. I locked it out, got my three white lights, meaning it was a good lift, and dropped the weight. When I put the weight down, I looked at my shoulder and watched my biceps tendon fall from the clavicle into my deltoid then down over my biceps. I walked calmly over to the PT they had at the event and said, "I think I just tore my biceps tendon." He asked if I was sure, and I assured him I had watched it drop. I got ice and called my mom.

The funny thing about calling home for me is that, since high school way back in my camp days, I was told not to call home unless something was wrong. My mother answered the phone and said, "What did you do now?" I told her and she said, "When are you going to learn? Isn't enough, enough already?" My answer was the same it was every other time I got hurt— probably not.

This surgery was pretty painful, because it required a screw drilled into my humerus to hold the scapula head of my biceps tendon in place so I would not have any deformities later in life. I didn't care about that. I had the surgery because the doctors said without it, I would probably have to stop weightlifting. *I don't think so.* In 2015, a year later, I would go on and compete in the Arnold Sports Classic held annually in Columbus, Ohio. I did not win, and I finally listened to Mark and did not try and cut body weight to get into a lower weight class, instead going into the meet competing in the heavier 85 kg weight-class as a lighter competitor. In my final competition, I got my highest ever snatch, hitting a 104 kg and a 127 kg clean and jerk (not my highest, but it was a win).

Unfortunately, my time with weightlifting came to an end because my left shoulder started giving me problems with my snatch, and work was finally starting to pick up with clients, so I had to make a decision to continue to work out elsewhere or to start earning a living. I had been weightlifting since 2006, and although I still enjoyed the competitive outlet, as I am getting older, I am beginning to listen to my body a tiny bit more, so I stopped competitive weightlifting. My training business was getting busier and more and more clients were coming to me for various goals. From 2015 to 2018, once again I found myself training competitive bodybuilders, a sport I had fallen in love with as a kid. My ultimate goal in life was to look like one of those guys.

As luck would have it, my client and friend Mark Price would convince me to do just that, only in a way that I liked, through a federation called Ohio Power-Building Association (OPBA). Someone Mark was following on Instagram was promoting this new federation, and Mark was grinding through the start of his competition and planted the seed. He suggested I do it because he felt I was strong and getting shredded for the pool together would be fun. I loved the idea and once again, I openly accepted the chance to push the envelope with two styles of training that generally are kept separate.

One thing I love is how the body responds to stress. Since I started my fitness journey I have always wanted to see how far I can push it. My workouts and my body are where I experiment. I have always tried to force my body to adapt to the demands of working out for sport, so what would be different now? This time, I was armed with all the years of experience and knowledge from my education. I could do it without thinking. Since the first show I did, I had gone through a master's program, gotten many certifications, and completed my Precision Nutrition certification. I could make this happen. I wasn't only going to tell people what to do to get the body for the stage; now I was going to put my money where my mouth was. At the time, I had also recently started a new relationship. Man, I love to complicate my life!

(2015, photo credit to Keith Harney)

I enlisted the help of a friend and a nutritionist from Washington State, whose information is at the end of this book. I used her help and diet to get back on track with my eating. After Thanksgiving in 2016, I was in a rut and nothing was working properly. I was not tracking my diet, and I was not taking my own advice. My work as a coach was becoming routine and I was struggling. I knew I needed to get back to my core values and practice what I preached, and drastic measures were coming. I have modified the plan she gave me to fit my needs, but I will always give good coaching and credit where it is due. Check her out at www.keypotentials.com. Following the modified meal plan, keeping the core six meals a day intact, and my training plan set to meet the powerlifting demands, I went to work.

Lifting heavy was familiar territory to me, and eating properly had been a norm for me since 2006, when my brother Joe and I made a bet that I couldn't lose 20 pounds before he gained five pounds of muscle. I won in six weeks. Mark had given me the goal; I only needed to refocus. My girlfriend loved the idea. I think we had been dating for a few months, and I had been dieting. Now, I was about to go into hardcore mode. I had reset my mind, and I would not be stopped. I lived for a competition to work toward. I was getting to combine the things I loved most—eating and working out—so for me, that is what Heaven feels like. Since 2006, I had been on a quest to be as fit as possible and as lean as possible. With a newfound outlook and a date— September 2, 2017—it was go-time. I remember the date, because it is both Joe G's and my uncle Frank Pedone's birthday. I wanted to demonstrate what determination, hard work, and sacrifice looked like. I wanted to be an example for my clients, and even though they don't desire to step on stage, I wanted to use myself as the end product of what can happen when you put in the effort.

I wound up winning second place overall and first in powerlifting! I was extremely pleased. Since bodybuilding is subjective, you can never truly know how the judges will score you. Powerlifting on the other hand, is the weight you lift divided by your body weight, and I came in lighter than most and lifted equal to everyone, putting me ahead of the game by numbers. My entire life has been in direct competition with larger individuals, and it was my time to demonstrate my prowess as a coach and lifter. Winning wasn't my goal this time. Rather, it was creating an example for those I coach to follow. I still firmly believe what my parents taught me as a kid—if I put in the work, the outcome will happen!

(2018, 2nd OPBA meet.
Photo credit to Aftermarq 495# dl at 154#)

FINDING MY PURPOSE

There are two great days in a person's life—
the day we are born and the day we discover WHY.

—William Barclays [3]

In January 2013, Joe Gernetzke and I, with the help of an accountant and a lawyer, filed our incorporation papers with the state of Ohio and opened our business, Sentinel Performance, LLC. The idea of Sentinel—much like this book—was to help dispel and shield the masses from the ridiculous claims of the fitness industry. We named the company Sentinel after ancient guardians who protected communities from imminent danger. These guardians would stand watch and alert those they protected of danger; they were the first line of defense. We felt strongly about our duty to protect those who don't know any better, using exercise as our weapon. To elicit the results our clients seek, we promote and teach proper nutrition habits and strength training techniques to ensure quality movements that help create mental fortitude . Since 2013, we have taught our philosophy to those we've worked with.

Teaching our philosophy eventually made me realize I had to practice what I preached. Somewhere between 2015 and 2017, I had figured out I was no longer an athlete and needed to be an example for the people I worked with. I believed that if I was going to run a fitness company, I could no longer be an average person. I wanted to help my clients by being the leader they needed, and that meant setting the example. In my role as the chief executive officer of the company, I knew I needed to change my ways. I could not coach people on health and fitness if I was going out to party on the weekends. As the head of a fitness company, it would be unacceptable not to be in great shape. So, I gave up drinking. I wanted to demonstrate with proper discipline in the gym and kitchen what was possible. I cook and prepare all my meals and rarely go out to "party" or eat. I try my hardest to make sure I am always prepared with home-cooked meals.

My development to confidence has been a long road, but through the newly found enjoyment of the long grinding workouts and the really hard ten-minute workouts that tend to break me down, I have found a new level of strength within my evolution. I have become someone who needs the suffering to understand the reward. I'm like a mad scientist—I experiment on myself before having others try it. When I was younger, I didn't get that. I was motivated for a singular purpose—to play a sport. While I understand this mindset of suffering for a reward is not for everyone, it has given me insight into my limitations and how to overcome them. As a result, I have developed this armor of confidence. Now I want to share this experience with others. Weight training is a key ingredient to my success, just as weight training will be a key ingredient to your success. No matter how many injuries I've sustained or surgeries I've gone through, I have learned that each pain has provided me with much more happiness, because each time I was able to rebuild myself stronger. Becoming stronger has given me so much confidence and made me understand that others need to experience this as well. I have now found my purpose: give others that same gift of confidence.

I have used my discipline for working out to embrace my role as a company owner. Discipline to perform the hard tasks makes running a company or any obstacle feel less daunting. I would even go as far as saying that in 2016, my metamorphosis was only truly beginning to take shape. It has been a long process and that is why I felt compelled to write this book. I didn't want anyone to have to endure nearly as much as I have to be ready for success. My experiences helped shape me and have propelled me to help others. All my experiences, were invaluable lessons to help me formulate the strategy of becoming good at the basics. I promise if you master the basics I am about to share with you, your workouts will lead you to new heights and greater confidence. You will be able to conquer anything as long as you master the basics. By no means does basic have to mean remedial; basics can be extremely difficult. There is no need to reinvent the wheel; it is a basic tool that if used properly makes life easier, so why try to recreate it? It's best to accept it and get the most out of it. I have learned throughout my life's journey to get the most out of the basics!

THE FOUNDATION

I n this next section I am going to discuss the exact
principles of five foundational movements—the
basics! If you master these foundational movements, you will be prepared for any type of training.
These five movements are truly the foundation for
every exercise in the gym today, which is why I have
chosen them. "The FAB 5 "are: the squat, the deadlift, the bench press, the pull-up, and the overhead
shoulder press. In the coming pages, I will break
down each exercise and explain them from A to Z.

Before going in-depth into each of the five
exercises, I thought I would introduce them to you
individually and give you a brief reason as to why
I selected these particular exercises as the FAB 5
exercises for you to incorporate in your routine.

The squat is one of the best exercises you can do if pressed for time. It truly works your entire body, no matter if you do it with super heavy weights or perform it with only your body weight. However, all squats are not equal, and for the purpose of this book, when discussing a squat, we will define a squat as when your butt hits your ankles, or, as I like to say, "ass to grass."

The second exercise is the deadlift. Unlike the squat, the weight is not on your body, but rather on the floor and your objective is to pick-up the weight without bending and rounding your spine. In your mind's eye, picture a dog going to the bathroom. For our purposes, it won't matter if you pull conventional or sumo; each will be discussed later. All that matters is that you drive the weight off the floor using your legs.

The third exercise is the bench press, cousin to the push-up and literally the only thing anyone ever asks when they discover you work out: "So, how much do you bench?"

The fourth exercise is the pull-up. This exercise is synonymous with strength because I tend to think in extremes. Please take a moment to envision being faced with the unfortunate event of horrific accident that has left you dangling off a cliff. Would you be able to pull yourself up to safety? Hence, the pull-up.

Last, but not least, is the overhead press. The overheard press is one of the hardest exercises you can ever perform in the gym. Literally, you are at a mechanical disadvantage when trying to press any load over your head with your tiny, flexible shoulders. To be able to perform this movement without wrenching your back or using your legs is a challenge in it of itself. I have always struggled with the overhead press in terms of profound hypertrophy gains or weight lifted. My personal best, prior to most of my shoulder injuries, was 205 pounds. I probably weighed 170 pounds.

Now that I have introduced the exercises, let's get on with the proper way to perform each.

THE SQUAT

When performed correctly, this exercise will tax your physical, mental, and neurological ability. It doesn't matter if there is a load lifted or you are working against gravity and only using your body weight. A squat is fundamental in our daily lives. Whether we are getting in and out of our car or standing up from our chair at work, we are performing a squat. You want to be good at it to save yourself trouble at the office. This movement is a triple extension exercise of the lower body: extension of the hips, knee, and ankle. Hip extension is when the hip starts closed and works to become open. During this part of the exercise, the knee is closest to the chest due to a decreased angle at the hip crease. Knee extension is the straightening of your leg. The angle of the knee is increasing. Ankle extension, in the sagittal plane (plane of motion, which creates a right and left side divide) is less straightforward. Extension at the ankle in this plane of motion is both dorsi flexion and plantar flexion. During the concentric (upward) phase of the squat you are pushing away from the ground, increasing the angle of the ankle joint or plantar flexion. Picture stepping on the gas pedal of your car and pushing the pedal away from you—that is plantar flexion.

Picture of triple extension

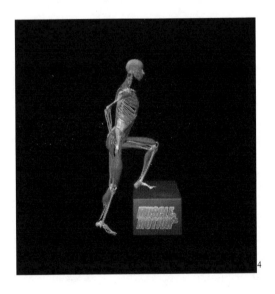

Can you see the squat weaving its way through your day already? Great! That is another reason I put it first; it truly is part of everyone's day. Now, a perfect squat is hard to envision if you've never really worked out before or have always shied away from them because you were afraid of loading your spine. I get it. Without weight, if you can sit your behind on your ankles, like a toddler, that is a perfect squat.

What happens is that as we age and get shackled to a desk, we lose that natural childlike ability to plop down and squat as we wish. We literally sit our way out of a squat. I am here to assure you, it's possible not only to get it back, but to keep it.

Performing a Squat

To perform the squat, you need to have a certain level of flexibility in your hips and ankles. If you are overly tight in either of those joints, performing a toddler-like squat will have to wait until after you have prepared your body a bit. Work on ankle mobility and hip opening stretches or activities to alleviate the stiffness from your day. For the purpose of this book, let's assume you are able to perform a bodyweight squat so your hips go below your knees, while your trunk is upright, and you can comfortably sit without raising your heels.

The old cue, "don't let your knees go in front of your toes" means not to raise your heels,. If you struggle with this, go ahead and practice it every day for 10-15 seconds throughout your day. You can even lean your butt up against a wall, gradually coming away from the wall, all the while being able to look straight ahead. Once you are comfortable with that position, you can start adding weight, I recommend a goblet dumbbell hold at first: hold the dumbbell underneath your chin (dumbbell head vertical).

The goblet hold is a cousin to the front squat due to the positioning similarities and will help ensure you remain upright. Once you can perform a goblet squat with 45 pounds or heavier, you are ready to try a bar. A standard male Olympic bar in the gym is 20 kg or 45 pounds, and a standard female Olympic bar is 15 kg or 35 pounds. Place the bar in one of two places: directly on top of your trap muscles (thick muscles just behind your head that look like shoulder pads on football players) or across your shoulder blades or mid-trap for a low bar squat (powerlifting technique). It doesn't matter which you prefer in terms of bar placement because both versions require the same moving parts. The main difference in bar placement is center of mass and the bar path you use. If you place the bar on top of your shoulders, your torso will be more upright; if placed on your mid-trap; your torso will lean forward more, forcing you to adjust your bar path since it is closer to your hip. High bar technique forces your bar to be closer to the knee and allows you to drop your hips further down. Regardless, the cues for the rest of the body are the same.

1. To perform a proper back squat, the bar is placed across your shoulders behind your head. You will need to set up the weightlifting

rack for the height of your shoulder and safety. To do that set the "J-hooks" or resting place for bar, at the appropriate shoulder height so you can easily walk the bar in and out of the rack without making contact with rack (called "catching a hook").

2. The best way to ensure your safety is to begin with a staggered stance to receive the bar from the rack across your shoulders. I prefer to perform squats this way because of ease of transition; I only need to move one foot. The staggered stance allows you to step weight up and back without making contact with the J-hook. Since they are always intentionally set lower than your shoulders, you won't have to worry about hitting the rack either to begin or finish the lift. Safety first and ego last.

3. Once you have unracked the loaded bar (weight), set your feet even, roughly hip-width apart—heels are hip width, toes are slightly further and turned out.

4. Prepare to brace. Breathe normally until you are ready to start your descent. Once you're ready, hold the last inhale, forcing the air against the wall of your abdomen and back. Use your diaphragm to force the air to pressurize your trunk from your belly button to spine. This is known as "the brace." It is necessary in all five of the exercises.

5. Descend as deep as you can go, ultimately trying to reach your butt or hamstrings to the back side of your calf, known as the bottom position. Once in the bottom position, spring back up, by maximally contracting the gluteus maximus and quadriceps, pushing your knees apart. Once you have "caught the bounce," you will return to standing. Repeat this for the number of reps and sets you have to perform that day.

6. To re-rack the weight, walk it forward and down into J-hooks. Never rise up onto your tip-toes to put it back. That will save your lifts when you're attempting to perform max effort and heavy attempts, such as a 1 repetition max (1RM).

Note: Always push out your knees. Having your knees collapse during a squat is a clear indication that there is a limitation in your body. Either a muscle is not properly engaged, or you are overly tight. Prior to performing any loaded squats, you should address any limitations with proper movement warm-up activities, known as movement preps. Movement prep exercise addresses deficiencies in your kinetic chain through a targeted effort. For example, to activate a weaker gluteus maximus you might perform some exercises with a Mini-Band around your knees, like clamshells or glute bridge.

Each of the aforementioned issues—ankle mobility, hip mobility, or knee collapse—are indicators of improper technique. Before you can truly master the squat, you must address these issues. If you have ankle mobility issues, address them early and consistently reinforce the mobility in your warm-ups; do the same with knee collapse or tight hips. These are learned movement patterns from either your work life or poor technique from years of improper form. I suggest you fix any issues before trying to lift heavier weights. The idea behind this is allowing your body to respond gradually to a step by step process of overload. In layman's terms, what you are trying to accomplish is adding stress to your body a little at a time. True mastery won't happen overnight and takes time. However, as long as you address any injury, imbalance, or limitation and remove your ego, you will progress. We are trying to get everything in your body stimulated and moving smoothly. Performing a squat in which your butt touches your ankles is hard but necessary for the health of your joints long-term, and that's what I am trying to focus on: long-term health of joints and long-term health in general so you can enjoy your life.

Proper Squat Technique with Bar:

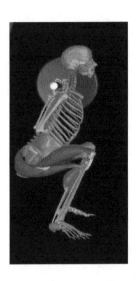

(Photo Credit to Keith Harney Photography 2020)

As I mentioned before, we tend to sit or stand throughout our day. Going from sitting to standing is a squat, so you have little to no excuse for not performing one. The reason the squat is so effective in training—besides the physical demands on your body—is because it is the perfect metaphor for life. Life is always demanding more from you. It is forcing more and more onto your shoulders, essentially weighing you down. From your family life to your job to balancing it all, you are being pushed farther and farther down, and that weight is heavy. The only thing you can do is stand up against it. Can you?

THE DEADLIFT

This exercise is appropriately named, since the weight is dead on the floor and your job is to bring it to life by lifting it up. I can tell you from experience that if you approach a heavy weight and your technique isn't perfect, it will feel as if the weight is nailed to the floor. Countless times you will be humbled by the weight when you focus on one aspect of the movement and not the entire thing. As with anything else, let your training play out. I try to record my lifts so I can break them down and watch myself over and over again to see if I can figure out what did or did not go right on each particular attempt. In competition, when attempting max effort, you have to trust your training and let your mind be free. (In competition, even after hurting my back, I was able to pull and hold 495 pounds for what felt like an eternity because I trusted my training. Although I couldn't lock out the rep, I was more than satisfied with my effort.)

The sumo deadlift and conventional deadlift objectively are the same. Besides the stance, the only difference is the effort or energy being displaced into the ground from your body. With the sumo stance, you have more of heel to glute drive, since the stance is spread out, while the conventional deadlift places more effort in the hamstring and lumbar area. If not performed correctly, you can really hurt yourself with a deadlift. A common mistake with the set-up is bar placement and limb interference. Normally, taller people have to go around their knees. Due to the length of the femur, they have more to get out of the way when performing a deadlift. However, if you address this at the start with your set-up, you should never have this problem. If you feel like you are too tall to deadlift or have issues getting your knees out of the way because you go around them and it places too much stress on your lumbar spine, then my suggestion would be to elevate the weight so the start position is slightly higher, using boxes or other plates to lift it up higher. Another way to address this would be starting with your hips higher. Don't sit to the bar as much, or use a squat form to start. The bar should always start over the toe box of your shoe or foot; mid-foot may be too close and just behind toes may be too far for some. You will need to play with your set-up to figure out what works for you, just like choosing between sumo and conventional stances; it's a preference that boils down to comfort. Once you sort out your set-up and style for lifting, the pull and work are the same.

Performing a deadlift

1. To begin set your feet first, and step to the bar, making sure it is over the toe box of your shoe. Make sure you feel comfortable and grounded. How you use your feet is paramount to how the lift is performed. If you feel like your feet are off, then the first pull will be a mess.

   a. In a sumo pull, use your feet to spread the floor.

   b. In a conventional deadlift, drive your feet into the earth, never allowing them to move.

2. Hand placement: In the conventional deadlift, slide your thumbs down your legs until you can grasp the bar. For sumo, the hands are inside your feet and can be shoulder-width apart, but this is also a preference for positioning. You must be comfortable.

3. Grip can be one of three styles: hooked grip, overhead, or mixed/alternated.

   a. Hook grip is Olympic lifting style, where you wrap the thumb around bar then hook over the top of it with your index finger and middle finger, locking in your grip. This is an advanced grip and not something I normally teach to beginners.

b. Conventional overhand grip will give you biggest disadvantage since you will be lifting with both hands gripping in the same direction. The limiting factor of grip means you can only lift what your hands can hold on to.

c. Mixed or alternated grip is a checks and balances type of grip—if one hand fails, the other can hold. Traditionally, this grip is the grip used by powerlifters for heavy maximum effort lifts.

4. Grasp the bar as you begin to lower your hips toward the bar. To pull the slack out of the bar, tighten your back muscles to prepare to lift the weight. Although your legs are doing the work, your upper body is a key component of a successful lift. Your ability to maintain your trunk rigidity and create a good brace as you did in the squat allows you to support your spine.

5. Lock your shoulders in by flaring your lats, thus taking the slack out of your arms and applying effort into the weight. Taking slack out of the bar is almost like a pre-lift, virtually applying force to the bar before you begin to use your lower body.

6. Lowering your hips to the bar (known as sinking your hips) creates a wedge between the earth and the weight. This effort will transform your body into a coiled spring, creating potential energy that you will use to explode into the bar to complete the movement.

7. To stand up, push your heels into the earth as if you are trying to explode vertically, driving the floor away. The creation of the wedge, or the hinge of the hip, should generate enough force to propel the bar vertically toward your hips. This is a very difficult concept. You should not try to yank the weight off the floor. By using the wedge technique, you are making your body into a powerful lever to overcome the inertia of the weight on the floor against gravity. You generate the force by creating tension through your hamstrings and glutes to power the hydraulic wedge you have just created.

8. For the descend, follow the same path you used to lift the bar off the floor to your hip back down to the ground. You should be careful to make sure not to drop the weight into your knees or to overly resist the weight as it descends back to rest. Let gravity allow the weight to bring you back down to the starting position. Once the weight is at complete rest, then perform the necessary sets and repetitions planned for the workout.

(Photo Credit to Keith Harney Photography 2020)

The reason you should always have the deadlift in your program is because of how it translates to your life. It is a very hard exercise, but when you can pull a weight off the floor equal to or heavier than your own bodyweight, you can accomplish anything. This exercise will give you confidence and strength to face just about anything in life without doubting yourself and without fear of failure. You know that if you do what you've trained for, you will succeed. The second reason to have this exercise in your routine, besides the physical benefits, is how often it is performed in any given day in your life. How many times have you picked something heavy up off the floor? It's not usually equal to your bodyweight but just awkward and cumbersome enough that it feels like it's glued down. The reality is, you are deadlifting!

Make your life easier, and prepare yourself for those movements. Give yourself the confidence to know you won't fail at picking up that air conditioner or moving the couch to clean the dust bunnies because you know how to deadlift properly. I have had all types of clients perform this movement—even the most reluctant of clients with complete fusion of his vertebrae (his c-spine, t-spine, and lumbar spine). His wife had just recently had a baby, and he needed to be able to pick up the car seat. I explained to him that the motion was a deadlift. So, I had him practicing it in the gym to make his life easier. After a few weeks, he was able to perform a deadlift up to 95 pounds for reps. if he can do it with complete fusion of his spine, what is your excuse?

THE BENCH PRESS

The bench press, for most people, is the standard by which your strength is measured. Ordinary people will never ask how much you can squat or what your best deadlift is. However, once you are labeled as a "meathead," a frequent gym-goer, or even a weightlifter, the very first question you will be asked is, "How much can you bench?"

I recall that very thing happening to me back in college. My mother's childhood friend came to visit. It was summertime, so I was on break and home. I was eating at the dining room table as the two gal-pals were telling one another of all their children's exploits. When my mother got to me, she was sharing about my football team and how much time I spent working out. Suddenly, there was an opening for my mom's friend—whose son was working out at the time—to speak to me.

"Oh, Frank, you work out now?" she asked.

As any teen would do, I grunted in an affirmative tone while eating, but what I really wanted to say was, "Duh, my mother just told you. I'm sitting right here listening." However, I didn't.

She then asked me, "So what do you bench?"

I was caught off guard, because I was confused as to why she would ask. Would she understand my answer? I said "315," and I will never forget her response.

"Is that good? My son can bench 225?"

I gave her a thumbs up and said, "Well, 315 is better than 225, so I'd say it's good."

I know, I know, I was a horrible bratty kid who should have been smacked, but I was dumbfounded by her question. She had no reference to ask the question other than that her son had benched 225. The point to this story is that normal people just ask to ask, never understanding the answer given. She was just being polite. Of course, I understand that now, but my mind at 18 years old was quite befuddled as to what she hoped to get from this exchange, other than me looking at her funny or being a smart ass.

In terms of technique, there isn't much to explain that hasn't been discussed in the previous two exercises. Hand placement on the bar is based on comfort, normally dependent on arm length. Longer arms tend to hold wider on the bar. Foot placement is where I will spend the majority of my time during this explanation.

I have seen many crazy things when it comes to benching, like having your feet up or moving your feet during the lift. The bench should be a total body exercise in that you lock your lower body into the ground for your upper body to perform the exercise. It is not dissimilar to the deadlift, where you are effectively locking your upper body in place to prepare to drive with your legs. Your feet should maintain contact with the ground in one of two ways—either the entire foot or the ball of your foot. This foot placement allows you to push into the ground, creating drive into your legs, and forcing your hips down into the bench. Lifting will always be about leverage. Why forfeit three-quarters of your ability to generate force and power by simply letting your feet flap around in the air? Create a strong base, locked into the ground and forcing your body against the bench, while simultaneously destroying the weights in the gym.

To perform the arch, you need leg drive forcing your t-spine in the bench. The small of your back comes up off the bench, thereby creating an arch, which allows the lifter to diminish the range of motion and permits the bar to come toward the sternum. The "arch" in powerlifting circles allows you to engage your lats and drive your shoulder (c-t-spine) into the bench to maximize force generation. Greater force generation from your body yields greater weight lifted. I understand your concern for not wanting to be a powerlifter, so we won't focus on the "arch." Simply know it's for your advantage.

Performing a bench press:

1. Your gaze should be on the inside of the bar, meaning your forehead and the bar are roughly even. Your shoulders should never be even or further back than the side of the bench uprights or rack.

2. Your feet should be firmly driven into the ground, creating a solid foundation. You should be on the balls of your feet or completely flat-footed. This position should be similar to the deadlift or squat foot position.

3. Your hands should be slightly wider than your shoulders, if not even. I always recommend that you begin with an empty bar (no weight plates) to practice grip and test where you want your hands before ever attempting a weighted bar lift.

4. To un-rack the weight, lift it out of the uprights with fully extended arms. The path of the bar should have a slight arch to it. Bring it toward your nipples, but no lower than your sternum. The start and finish position is full extension of the arm. Prior to the descent of the bar, inhale, and create the brace as you

have been instructed to with your squat and deadlift.

5. As pictured below, the bar path is a slightly curved line. The bar path should not be a straight line coming from the rack toward your neck.

6. Touch your body with bar and pause for a 2-one thousand count. Then press the bar up, locking the bar out with full extension at the elbow. Then place it back in rack if the set is over. If not, repeat for repetitions as programmed.

BENCH PRESS
BAR POSITIONING & BAR PATH

The bench press has always been an exercise that is led by ego. I am certainly guilty of that. I would highly recommend you put your ego aside and focus on the importance of joint health and maximal contraction of the pectoralis major. When performing any exercise in the gym, if you can place your mind in that muscle belly and truly envision the effort and energy being used, the exercise will become more potent, and the weight being lifted won't matter. Once again, if you master the technique with no flaws in your movement patterns, the weights themselves will virtually increase on their own, giving you the confidence to continue to push your limits!

(Photo Credit to Keith Harney Photography 2020)

THE PULL-UP

The next exercise, the pull-up, can be difficult for the average person. Most of the clients I have had over the years shared it as their biggest goal: to perform a pull-up. I can't remember when I began doing them; I would imagine it was in high school. For me, the pull-up was never a thing, maybe because I focused all my attention on being strong. When it finally came time to perform one, I was simply able to. I don't really recall ever struggling with the ability to do one. What I do remember is back in Brooklyn when I worked out at Dolphin on Avenue N with my best friend, Matt, we witnessed a massive Marine performing pull-ups. He had four plates strapped on his waist and was absolutely crushing pull-ups as wide as his hands could go on the bar. On that day, all I remember is wanting to be able to do pull-ups from a dead hang with two plates, or 90 pounds, on my body.

To perform the pull-up, a lot of people fail to understand that first you need a strong latissimus dorsi or "lat" to begin the movement, a strong core to control the movement, and solid grip strength to continue to perform reps of the movement. The majority of the people I encounter that set pull-ups as a goal usually don't understand these above concepts.

First, let me address the use of the latissimus dorsi. This muscle is huge. It runs almost the length of your back and when recruited should bring your elbow toward your body. It also functions to push your arm away from your body. Another effective way to train the lat is through eccentric movement patterns. Eccentric means the negative phase of a movement, where a stretch and muscle contraction are happening simultaneously. A common issue I have found is the lack of ability to create tension in the lat. When working with my clients, they have always said they feel pull ups in their hand grip or their biceps. The reason for that is because they understand how to utilize their hands or biceps but lack the understanding to engage their lats properly, either from lack of understanding the movement or from not training other movements properly. For example, to perform the lat pull down exercise, your focus should be on sitting upright, with a slight lean back from the hips, driving your elbows to your ribcage, using the lat to pull the weight down to your chest. By placing your mind in your armpit, so to speak, you create the ability to adduct (bring together) your scapula (shoulder blades), creating the correct movement. Think of windshield wipers moving back and forth in a curved line. You should never merely start yanking the weight down by bending your elbows and pulling the weight toward your chest—this is ineffective at best.

To perform a perfect pull-up, or strict pull-up, you must start from a dead hang with full extension of the arms. Your legs can be bent or straight but should not move to aid in the ability to pull your chin to the bar. Ultimately, you should be able to pull your chest all the way up to the bar from a dead hang. To perform a strict pull-up, you will need good grip strength, a solid core connection so your body doesn't move, and a strong mind-muscle connection to your lat. The biceps are a secondary mover in that they will contract to flex the elbow, bending the joint and nothing more. More bicep curls won't necessarily help your lat contract to perform a proper pull-up.

All other versions of a pull-up out there are not real pull-ups for the purpose of this book. I demand strict, dead hang pull-ups from my clients. If you cannot perform repetitions of a strict pull-up, changing it to make it easier will not get you better. Performing assisted pull-ups without understanding how to engage or recruit your lat to perform a pull-up is also an ineffective training method. You have to learn how to perform a proper pull-up before you can teach yourself something else. The best way to learn how to perform a pull-up is to start by hanging from a bar—just hang, nothing more. Once you can hang there for 30 seconds to a minute, you can then start from the top, chin over bar and slowly lower yourself, performing a negative pull-up. A negative pull-up as mentioned earlier is the eccentric phase of the movement. Here, you are actively firing the muscle (contracting the lats) while simultaneously stretching it, eventually succumbing to gravity. Perform a negative pull-up before you ever try to assist yourself with the use of machines or bands. The assistance becomes a crutch, and you will not learn how to perform a pull-up properly with an assistance alone.

To perform a pull-up, you only need your body and a bar set higher than you are tall. Once you can perform three to four rounds of five-second negative pull-ups, I believe you will be ready to attempt three or four rounds of 1 to 2 reps. First, learn the variations of a negative, and then add assistance to practice full range pull-ups before you attempt any unassisted version. Get yourself comfortable, so if you struggle with pull-ups, you will need to perform these two exercises to learn.

Performing a proper strict pull-up

1. Set your hands wider than your shoulders, only slightly wider to begin. As you get better and more comfortable, you can begin to widen your hand placement. The wider you place your hands the greater the force needed to begin and maintain the movement.

2. From a hanging position, whether you step up or jump up to the bar, the movement must be done from a complete hang. Inhale and create your brace as in the other exercises.

3. Without yanking, control your body ascent. As you begin to rise, you should focus on driving your elbows to your ribcage with a forcible contraction of your lats.

4. Pull your chin over the bar, or chest up to the bar. Then gradually allow your body to go back to the full extension at the elbow. It is that simple.

5. There is no momentum being used, or swinging involved, no quarter reps. It is full extension from a dead hang with little to no movement taking place from the rest of your body. That is what you will need the brace for, to control the rest of your body from swinging.

TIP: When you can perform four sets of ten reps of these, you can then change variables to make them more difficult or challenging. You can change the grip, pre-fatigue the muscle belly, or tax your grip beforehand, all the while lifting your body and nothing more. Of course, if you are a sadist like me, you can add weight and try to perform the movement with 90 pounds up to double bodyweight for fun!

(Photo Credit to Keith Harney Photography 2020)

Earlier, I briefly discussed the ability to perform a pull-up in the worst-case scenario of a car crash that leaves you hanging off a cliff. As a coach, and a fairly fit coach, I try to help my clients really envision scenarios that place them in real-world situations. I try to create a picture of worst-case scenarios when I first meet them to elicit a response that is real, raw, and honest. Most of my clients, when discussing what strength means to them, state it as an ability to lift an object, yet the object is rarely ever themselves. When confronted with the notion of performing a pull-up in the gym, most beginners scoff at the idea and quit before they tried, knowing they have never had the ability, but they never put themselves in a life or death scenario. Most people tend never to think about a loved one being in harm's way. Being an extreme individual, if faced with that scenario myself, I don't want my children to ever fear I can't save them. It is a situation I will prepare for, hoping it never happens, but if both of our lives literally hang in the balance, I will save both of us. My goal is to train for the ridiculous off-chance that I am faced with that scenario one day, so I know I could do it, because I am strong enough. I don't look at the pull-up like a remedial task in the gym; I look at it as if my life depends on it. Suddenly there is a new, more visceral desire to perform this basic movement because it forces a person to look at strength as life or death. So, take control of your life and build your confidence one pull-up at a time.

THE OVERHEAD PRESS

The overhead press, the strict press, or the military press—whatever name you give to this exercise—the objective does not change. You will take a weight or an object and lift it over your head. It is one of the most difficult lifts to perform in the gym. The muscles of the shoulders are smaller in comparison to those in the chest or back. The shoulder joint is a ball and socket joint and is considered a very flexible joint with a very large range of motion (ROM). A normal healthy shoulder should be able to achieve 180 degrees of motion.

The purpose of the overhead press is to take a load, usually a weighted bar, and lift it straight over your head without using momentum, i.e., the push press. This particular exercise puts you at a huge disadvantage due to how a healthy shoulder joints function. Remember, your shoulder is a joint that is supposed to achieve great ROM, so musculature is normally less adaptive to hypertrophy or growth. This exercise isn't only about the shoulder muscles, known as the deltoids (medial, lateral, posterior). It is an exercise about your total body effort, from your connection to the ground with your feet to your hands on the bar. If you have a weakness, this exercise will expose it. Therefore, it has earned its place as the last exercise of the FAB 5.

Performing the overhead press

1. Grasp the bar with your hands even or just outside of shoulder width. Usually on Olympic bars there is knurling (grooves cut into bars for friction and grip) that help indicate proper and comfortable hand placement.

2. Unrack the bar the same as you would with the squat, only this time you will be holding the bar in front of your neck, across your collar bones.

3. From here, when you are ready to perform your first rep, inhale and create your brace. Hold your breath, pushing it down and against your spine with your diaphragm. This will pressurize your trunk to stabilize your spine, just as with the other four exercises.

4. In one motion, extend your arms over-head, locking out your elbows, and driving the weight directly over the crown of your head. Your armpits should be close to your ear lobes; this position is called "listening to your armpits."

5. Slowly lower the weight back down to your rack position and repeat for prescribed sets and reps of your program.

6. Do not lean back, arch, or overextend the spine to perform any repetition. You should be standing upright, with a stacked spine (neutral spine) to the best of your ability for each rep. If your form breaks down, do not attempt more reps. Simply stop, recover, and rest, and then begin again.

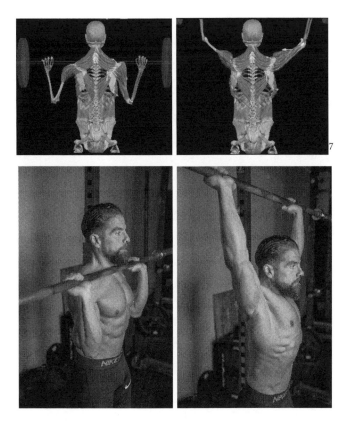

(Photo Credit to Keith Harney Photography 2020)

When performed correctly, you should feel this movement in your shoulders, core, and lats. This exercise is truly a testament to a well-balanced physique. As I mentioned above, it requires you to understand how to set your feet. The placement of your feet and the firm contact with the ground will maximize your press. This will take practice. It will be hard to perform reps without using momentum from your legs as you begin to fatigue. The grounding of your feet is similar to the way you set your feet for your bench press or how you lock in your shoulders during the deadlift. Even though movement is not taking place there, the lift cannot happen without a truly strong foundation. The reason this exercise is last is because it requires a strong foundation built through the rest of the five exercises to perform it appropriately. This exercise will take the most time to see significant hypertrophy and strength increases, but just like with the other exercises, the impact on your daily life will be immediate once you master it.

THE PROGRAM: "THE FAB 5"

N ow that I have explained the five fundamental exercises and their purposes, I can help you begin to create a program for yourself. The purpose for this style of programming is to master these exercises and take back your life outside of the gym. The program should be performed after you have met certain mobility requirements. If you struggle with issues such as knee collapse or pronation/ supination (rolling of ankle) during squats, first address those issues. Any issues of mobility should be addressed prior to implementation of the full program below. Again, these exercises will be the foundation and majority of your workout program, therefore it would behoove you to address functionality and limitations before implementing a full program. With that being said, I will assume you have addressed basic mobility and are ready to begin.

This program is to help you master these five exercises, making them mainstays in your day to day programming. All other exercises performed will be accessory or parts to the five movements. For example, on bench day you will perform two movements for the chest other than the bench press, like the push-up and dumbbell fly. These are known as accessory exercises. In this way, all work being performed on that day will be geared toward reinforcing the same movement pattern and muscle recruitment. The repetitious nature of the movements allows for you to practice volume without overdoing one specific movement. The unique nature of this style of programming allows for tremendous variation due to the plethora of exercises you can choose to accompany the five fundamental exercises.

The accompanying exercises are considered accessory work because they are similar to the core movement. Each accessory exercise should be chosen to excite the primary muscles and motion of the fundamental exercise as well as the smaller, secondary muscles, motion, and stabilizers. This design will give you the most benefit and repetitions to train and learn the proper movement patterns. Movement patterns are the body's ability to perform a task with little to no guessing. Most people commonly refer to this as muscle memory. Muscles can either contract or relax. The body's ability to contract a muscle faster is in part due to the neurological pathway. The quicker the body can excite the muscles, the more learned the movement becomes, meaning the more you perform an exercise, the easier it will become to excite the working muscle bellies. The neuromuscular maps have been laid down, and now you only have to use them, so to speak. The faster the body can excite the neurons to contract or relax in that muscle belly, the smoother and more controlled the action becomes—hence, learned movement. The more practiced a pattern, the better and more proficient the pattern becomes.

Strength training should be a progressive process with one variable being changed at a time. The mega-successful style of CrossFit uses a constantly varied programming which can only work well when a movement pattern is so proficient it can be manipulated in other ways to illicit a change. The program style I have mapped out using the FAB 5 will make you become proficient in the basic movements, thus giving you a solid foundation to perform any other workout style you desire—once you've become a master. I will not consider you a master until you can perform each of the five movements with your bodyweight for several sets and reps. Performing any of these movements with your bodyweight for one repetition means you are just getting started.

In the coming pages, I will do my best to list out all accessory exercises for each of the five fundamentals

(FAB 5). I will also map out a sample workout and breakdown of workout routines, called splits, for two to five days per week, known as a micro-cycles. Each training week, or micro-cycle, will give you an idea how to map out the plan that suits your schedule. The idea is to fold the routine seamlessly into your daily life. If you know you really can't commit to three or five days a week for your routine, I will address that specifically. I believe strength training is a must and will permeate the rest of your life, giving you the confidence to accomplish any task. So, I strongly suggest you make 45-minute blocks of time daily to commit to yourself and commit to taking back your life. Being active is a large component of this lifestyle switch, but strength training is the main component. Running is not considered a workout; it is an activity. You absolutely require strength training in order to run optimally, and therefore, for the purposes of this book, running alone is not a workout.

Strength training requires an external stimulus, and if you are trying to lose weight or build muscle, running alone won't help. What running will do is decrease the number on the scale. That is largely due to the body's desire for decreased weight bearing on the joints during increased movement. When you run, your body will not hold on to excess weight, it will "lighten the load" in order to take pressure off the joints. The load is not exclusive to just fat either; it is also going to burn muscle to save the joints. Any excess weight the body can shed, it will. The only issue I have with this is that as we age, our bodies' muscle mass decreases as well. The best defense for this process, known as sarcopenia, is weight training. The muscle activation and recruitment during weight training forces the body to retain more muscle because of use. Maintaining muscle mass will inevitably prevent injuries and keep sarcopenia at bay for longer. Research also favors weight training over cardiovascular workouts largely due to the prolonged effects of calorie burn after each bout of training. While cardio workouts will burn more calories immediately, there is research that demonstrates a far more significant calorie expenditure "burn" on resting metabolism after a strength training session[8]. To transform your body truly, you will have to focus on the mastery of the basics combined with cardiovascular workouts and a healthy diet. There is no magic pill!

Accessory Exercise List (10 options each)

Squat:
- Leg press (hack, sled, selectorize)
- Knee extension (single, double)
- Split squat
- Step up
- Box jump
- Lunge (lateral, forward)
- Goblet squat
- Sumo squat
- Belt squat
- Zercher squat

Deadlift:
- Glute bridge
- Romanian deadlift (RDL)
- Jefferson deadlift
- Hamstring curls
- Snatch grip deadlift
- Rack pull
- Hip thruster
- Bulgarian split squat
- Lunge (drop/reverse, curtsey/crossover)
- Nordic hamstring curl

Bench Press:
- Dumbbell bench press (flat or incline)
- Incline press
- Machine chest press (selectorize)
- Dumbbell fly (flat or incline)
- Cable fly
- Cable press
- Banded press
- Dips
- Push-up (close grip, wide grip)
- Triceps extension (cable, skull crusher)

Pull-up:
- Lat pull-down (wide grip, neutral grip, reverse grip)
- Dumbbell row (single, double)
- Bent over row (barbell, dumbbell)
- Machine row, cable row—seated
- Chin-up

- Dumbbell curls
- Barbell curls (easy bar, barbell, fixed weight)
- Cable curls
- Single arm lat pull down (cable or machine) (usually if machine it is free weight leverage type)
- High pull to face

Overhead Press:
- Dumbbell strict press (standing or seated)
- Arnold press
- Dumbbell raises (lateral, reverse, frontal)
- Cuban press
- Behind the neck (military press)
- Upright row
- Kickbacks (banded, dumbbell, machine)
- Shrugs
- Overhead hold
- Muscle snatch (barbell) or dumbbell power snatch

Please note: Each of the above exercises can be performed in a partial lift, a negative lift, a concentration or concentric only movement, therefore changing the stimuli of the movement. Although I have only listed ten movements, once you understand how to perform one version, there are countless variations of each. I stopped at ten to keep it simple for the novice lifter.

Two Day Split Routine: Suggested

This routine will require two strength workouts a week. During each workout, you will split the FAB 5 into push and pull exercises for simplicity purposes.

WORKOUT 1

Day 1
  Squat
  Two accessories (forward lunge, knee extensions)
  Bench press
  Add one accessory (incline dumbbell bench press)
  Overhead press
  One triceps exercise (cable push downs)—not
    mandatory

  1-mile walk

Day 2
  Deadlift
  Two accessories (Romanian deadlift (RDL), ham-
    string curls)
  Pull-up
  Two accessories (single arm row, lat pull down)
  One biceps exercise (dumbbell curl)—not
    mandatory

  1-mile walk

  -OR-

WORKOUT 2

Day 1
Bench
Two accessories (incline dumbbell press, cable flies)
Overhead press
Two accessories (Arnold press, lateral fly)
Triceps exercise (dips)
Squat

1-mile walk

Day 2
Deadlift
Three accessories (Bulgarian split squat, Romanian Deadlift, hip thruster)
Pull-up
Three accessories (lat pull down, single arm row, chin-up negative)

1-mile walk

Explanation of WORKOUT 1

Workout 1 begins on Day 1 with the squat (a triple extension lower body movement) with two corresponding accessories exercises (forward lunge and knee extension). Lunges are also a triple extension exercise of the lower body, however, now we are adding in some complexity, with the unilateral component of this exercise. The knee extension can be performed unilaterally or bilaterally (one leg or two legs) and is a single joint exercise. This exercise specifically targets the quadriceps muscle. During both the lunge and the squat, the quadriceps will be recruited and fatigued, so this exercise will only repeat the activation of the muscle belly. Forcing a fatigued muscle to contract and relax will maximize the neurologic pathways that had previously been laid down. A repeat motion allows for the body to fire neurons of the same nerve endings consistently, making muscle contractions happen quicker and therefore becoming a learned movement pattern.

The idea is to ask the body the same question in different ways to facilitate mastery of the movement. The same idea happens with the bench press and overhead press. However, since those two movements require and recruit the shoulder joint, we need to focus our attention on not overworking the joint. So, I made the decision in this instance to decrease the accessory exercises. You will also notice the addition of the triceps exercise; it's not a must, but it allows you to continue to reinforce movement patterns. In the upper body, the extension of the elbow happens through contraction of the heads of the triceps (a secondary mover in both the bench press and overhead press). Adding in this singular exercise will specifically target the triceps through extension. This is not mandatory, but merely a recommendation for those that want a little more arm sculpting!

Day 2 begins with the deadlift (another triple extension exercise), only this time the emphasis is on the posterior chain of the body, or the pull muscles. Again, the idea here is to work the compound exercise as a whole, then reinforce it with parts to the whole. This means breaking down the movement and identifying a particular muscle group or joint of the movement to add a more focused singular effort. While the deadlift is a complete, full-body compound movement, the Romanian deadlift or RDL is only a portion of the same movement, with focus on the hip hinge. The hip hinge is the top aspect of the deadlift, with no extension or flexion of the knee joint. The emphasis is being placed on the hip joint and all musculature surrounding both the hip and the lumbar spine. Following the same rules as Day 1, we then perform the pull-up with the accessories. The reason for this split of all pressing exercises and all pulling exercise is for simplicity and overlap. Each movement and its corresponding exercises will allow for similar questions to be asked of the nervous system, allowing you to capitalize on the neuron synapses that innervate and excite each muscle belly.

Explanation of WORKOUT 2

Workout 2, Day 1 emphasizes the upper body since the squat exercise is the only lower body exercise. It is okay to place the squat exercise on its own if you load the movement pattern appropriately. You will need to perform enough sets and reps that you can create the overload stimulus we are after on the central nervous system (CNS). In the second workout for the week, I chose to make sure the lower body movements have more of an emphasis; they were performed first, then created more repetitions thereafter.

In Workout 2, Day 2 the bench press and overhead press exercises are being performed back to back with their individual accessory exercises. As you tax your energy levels, you want to be conscious of creating a plan that allows you still to have energy for the rest of your day, so you must plan accordingly. The idea of keeping it simple with three to four good quality sets of squats will reinforce your focus on mastery of form. You are in the gym to help you create the ultimate foundation for success outside the gym.

In Workout 2, Day 2, there are four total lower body movements. The first is the deadlift, again a triple extension movement of the ankle, knee, and hip joint. Remember, the idea is to start with the total body compound movement, followed by Bulgarian split squats, Romanian deadlifts and hip thrusters. This breakdown will focus on the hips, so the muscles that are required to function will mostly be of the posterior chain—glutes and hamstrings. In a Bulgarian split squat, your front leg will be performing a single leg squat with the rear foot elevated. This places the emphasis on the front leg, working both the posterior and anterior muscles of leg as you stand up—extension of the ankle, knee and hip.

The upper body movements for Day 2 are all geared toward working your latissimus dorsi (lats). The goal is to work the shoulder joint in the reciprocal motion of Day 1. Again, I want to create balance of joint motion and not overwork the joints in any one direction. Here, I have four movements planned, but if you counted, there are five pushing movements. Of course, don't forget how much stability and energy you will be using to perform the deadlift properly. Although it seems like the shoulder is performing one more extension exercise, we have more shoulder retraction and stabilization going on to perform both the deadlift and Romanian deadlift (which is the top half of the deadlift that focuses on hip hinge).

Note: The great thing about the simplicity and the never-ending variations of this style of programming is that it allows the freedom to plug and play multiple exercise variations to achieve the goal. This approach will allow for adjustments each week if there are limited repetitions from the week before, as well as give the user the ability to create a meso-cycle (a month or longer) focused plan, *i.e.*, an upper body versus lower body focus for four to eight week-long blocks. As long as you create balance overall throughout your variations, you will be able to recover before each workout. Due to the fundamental principles of placing all pull exercises together and all push exercises together, you will never be working the same joint in the same direction twice. This style of programming allows you to train every other day, if you wish, without overtraining.

Three Day Split Routine: Suggested

For a three-day workout plan, you can put more emphasis on fewer exercises per day with the workload being placed solely on the fundamental exercises. You have the choice of how to break up the work week. You can perform one strength workout out every other day and simply continue to cycle the workouts. You can take the weekends off to spend more time with your loved ones using a Monday, Wednesday, and Friday breakdown. Of course, you can use Tuesday, Thursday, and Saturday routine as well. How you plan out your week is up to you; the workouts should resemble something similar to the below set up.

Day 1:
>   Push upper body, pull lower body
>   Bench press
>   Three accessories (fly, dip, incline press)
>   Deadlift
>   Three accessories (hip thruster, glute bridge, hamstring curl)
>
>   1-mile walk

Day 2:
>   Lower body push, upper body pull
>   Squat
>   Three accessories (leg press, step up, frontal lunge)
>   Pull-up
>   Three accessories (lat pull down, barbell row, single arm row)
>
>   1-mile walk

Day 3:
>   Overhead press
>   Four accessories (upright row, lateral raises, frontal raises, Arnold press)
>   Triceps exercises (cable push downs)
>   One major lower body exercise of choice—squat or deadlift variation (Bulgarian split squats)
>
>   1-mile walk

Workout Explanation

Due to having more time in the gym, you have the ability to spread the exercises through the course of the week. Each person, when deciding how they want their week to look, needs to make some decisions based on their goals and consideration for their time. The suggested workouts I wrote are based on creating balance of joints across the board. Balance can be a very individualized thing. For instance, I have shoulder issues, so I would want to isolate the shoulder workout on its own day. Someone else may struggle more with deadlifts or squats, causing them to plan to isolate those movements. That is the great thing about this approach to create your program. Organization is based on *your* goals, as long as you keep to the structure and focus the workouts based on mastery of the FAB 5. You can easily create a program. You don't have to be a personal trainer or strength coach to understand how to structure your workout, if you adhere to the fundamentals. Still to come is the step-by-step metrics of manipulating the variables to reap the benefits.

Four Day Split Routine: Suggested

Day 1:
  Squat
  Two accessories (forward lunge with dumbbell
     hold*, knee extension)
  Shoulder press

Two accessories (dumbbell lateral raises, shrugs)

1-mile walk
Holding the dumbbells will use your shoulders, giving you a little extra benefit for this combination.

Day 2:
Upper body Pull
Pull-up
Two accessories (bent over row, 1 arm row)

1-mile walk

Day 3:
Deadlift
Two accessories (Romanian deadlift, hamstring curl)

1-mile walk

Day 4:
Bench press
Two accessories (incline dumbbell press, cable flies)

1-mile walk

Workout Explanation

Ultimately, how you break up the movements is completely up to you. I tried to make sure to separate the lower body exercises from the upper body exercises by placing an alternate movement in between each day. The only overlap for the shoulder joint is pushing (overhead press) and pulling (pull-up) day that follow one another. However, if you remember, this is reciprocal joint action, so you will be working the synergistic muscles of the joint on alternate days; so, as they say, "this is kosher." The placement of the fifth FAB 5 exercise is entirely up to you. I placed it on one of the two lower body days, as not to work a pre-fatigued joint, but you could very well argue to place it on any day. For example, you could decide to give overhead press its own day, placing another of the FAB 5 with squats. The freedom of choice is what makes this style of programming a luxury. You will never be wrong, as long as the quality of work doesn't suffer.

Five Day Split Routine

The five-day split routine allows you to separate each movement into its own day. You can also choose to perform more accessory work if you feel you are ready. For the novice lifter, I would suggest no more than two or three accessories until your movement patterns are perfect. I consider myself an advanced lifter, and even I struggle with perfection at times, so working the form and quality of movement becomes my priority for each of the FAB 5 exercises. Life tends to get in the way of the perfect workout, so if you can plan and focus on good reps through each of the FAB 5, you will get everything you need and more. As I have mentioned, I suffer from chronic shoulder pain which ultimately inhibits my mobility, thereby creating poor shoulder rhythm. My left scapula does not properly adduct or abduct causing very limited flexion or extension of my left shoulder joint. It's a blessing when the pain subsides and allows me to perform an overhead shoulder press. Even if it is just the bar, that is more than enough stimuli to tax my system because of how deteriorated the rhythm of the shoulder is. The reps I perform now versus pre-shoulder injury don't look the same at all, but they sure do feel the same.

VARIABLES

I know what you are thinking; the above seems to be missing a lot of information. Step one is to plan out what you want to do, step two is to learn how to manipulate the variables. There are tons of variables you can manipulate to change the impact of each workout. When planning a routine, people often tend to change too many variables at once, frequently leading to an injury. I would caution you to move properly first. Teach your body the patterns. When you can successfully perform the movements repeatedly, you can add a variable.

Variables include:
- speed of movement (tempo)
- frequency of movement

- increase or decrease of loads
- increased or decrease range of motion
- increased complexity
- duration of each movement
- number of sets
- number of reps
- super-sets
- pre-fatigue movements (supersets of same joint action, or decreased rest intervals, etc.)

Each of these variables should be added one at a time. Once you add one and master the movement, add a second and so on. Each addition of a variable should be used without ever changing the exercises you have selected from day one. The addition or subtraction of a variable will change the stress of the workout by itself.

I offer an example to demonstrate variable implementation. First, perform a max effort squat (best squat you can for one rep) followed immediately by a secondary exercise, body weight squats to failure. In this example, not only are you stressing the body with the max effort squat, but you then increase fatigue of the same joints and muscle groups, creating even higher levels of stress on the body. In this example, let's say during the first week you perform this super-set, you can squat 200 pounds for one rep followed by 20 bodyweight squat reps. The second week you attempt this, you again work up to a 200-pound squat, then you are able to squeeze out 25 bodyweight squats. Since you were able to perform 25 good quality squats, you decide to add a weight the next time to a second squat. Then you are doing a goblet squat—a new move. The third week you attempt this workout, you again perform a 200-pound squat, then 10 goblet squats—with a light weight under the chin. Congratulations! You have successfully manipulated multiple variables—load, super-set, and pre-fatigue.

Let's continue to learn variable manipulation by further changing the above example. Now we will change the organization a bit, placing the goblet squats before your max effort back squat attempt. Here, you will pre-fatigue the actual squat effort of the one repetition attempt (1RM). Remember, this is without changing either exercise. You perform 25 goblet squats before you attempt the max effort squat. Before we continue, how do you believe your max effort attempt will be impacted? Do you believe it will be even more or less challenging then before? Allow me to answer: if the max effort attempt of 200 pounds is truly your max effort, and you pre-exhausted your body before attempting the barbell squat, you should not expect to complete the rep. You should expect failure.

This method forces your body to adapt or fail to perform. If you perform this routine for the next four weeks, each time failing with 200 pounds, you have again successfully manipulated variables. By week five, if you do away with the goblet squats and pre-exhaustion of muscles and retest your back squat, you should see an increased max effort attempt. In theory, you should be able to perform a new max of 210 pounds—all because you appropriately understood how to illicit adaptation through variable manipulation.

You asked very specific questions of your body under duress, then gave your body time to understand the questions, respond, and create a change. Eventually, you repeat the first question: What is the one rep max (1RM)? In this last example, you subtracted the pre-fatigued movement, a variable, which decreases the intentional stress. That subtracted variable should allow you to prepare for an increased load attempt on your max effort squat. This increased load is all made possible through a solid understanding of variable manipulation and sticking to the basics. These are simple techniques to force the body to adapt.

In strength training, you have to create a plan that follows sound logic and moves step-by-step to increase the stimulus on your body. You do not ever really need to change more than one aspect. I always tell my clients that weight increases are earned. Demonstrate a strong understanding of the movement I am asking you to perform, and then we can change a variable. Poor execution upon change is expected. We are asking a new set of questions, and your body may or may not understand that right away. After the change, you may experience more soreness, or you may fatigue sooner than you had been. That is OK; it is to be expected when the stimuli are changed. Each time you change a variable, it changes how you are asking your body to perform that exercise. Performing a squat at max effort is considerably different than performing a bodyweight squat, however, they are both lower body triple extension exercises. Performing a push-up is different from performing a bench press, yet they are both horizontal shoulder flexion exercises. The difference between the two examples I just mentioned is load, a variable that can change any exercise stimulus. Your goal for the FAB 5 exercises is to be able to perform each exercise with the external load of your bodyweight. For an ordinary person to perform these five movements with bodyweight is considered remarkable; you can call yourself strong. At the end of the day, that is the goal: to be able to lift your body through your life.

Nutrition Guidelines

NOTE: I am not a nutritionist. If you want to speak to anyone regarding nutrition, please contact a licensed professional nutritionist or dietician (preferably with RD after their name). A licensed professional can provide you with the proper information and give you conclusive dietary information specific to your individual needs.

As I mentioned earlier; your diet should be the fuel you consume for the day. For whatever reason, dieting has always had a negative connotation attached to it. There is a perception that a diet is a long list of things you can't eat. In truth, your diet is everything you consume to give you energy for the day. Systematically, I believe, we have begun to eat with our eyes, noses, and other senses. No longer are we as a society working manual labor jobs, so the necessity of heavy calorie dense meals is gone. Nowadays, most jobs are done sitting at a desk, staring at a computer. In fact, we now have to schedule in breaks and remind ourselves to go eat and be physical. We have become tied to our desks and have sedentary lifestyles based on our technological advances, but at what cost?

To make your life easier, I am going to give you some steadfast rules to help you understand how to eat healthy. While I am aware of the many different diet trends out there, I am going to teach you how to eat for health, and not simply to get a number on the scale. The food you will be told to consume will be the fuel for your day and your workouts with the FAB 5 routine. I will not give you a large list of things not to do, but rather a short list of rules to follow. I will make this simple for you to apply it to your life, as if you were teaching the rules to your own children (which, at the end of this, I hope you do).

Rules to follow for healthy eating habits

1. Naturally occurring foods first
2. Fewer hands
3. Water is life-giving
4. Balance
5. Moderation

Explanation of Rules

Rule 1. Naturally occurring foods.

The best way to know what you are eating is to know what you are eating. If it grows from the earth or lives on the earth, you can eat it. This means whole foods. Foods grown from soil that make their way to your table, like barley, wheat, tomatoes, potatoes, rice, corn, beans, nuts, lettuce, broccoli, cauliflower, kale, spinach, bananas, watermelon, apples, oranges, grapefruit, pineapple, etc., are all good to be consumed. Animal products that are butchered and make their way to your table, like pork, fish, chicken, beef and lamb are also good to consume in your diet. Since humans are omnivores, we have a large breadth of foods to choose from, so try not to limit yourself. While I understand there are individuals who can't eat certain foods, I am merely trying to simplify what you look at for fuel. What you choose to eat is up to you as long as it is naturally occurring. I am also not advocating an organic diet, I am simply saying that if you are pressed to make a decision between eating rice or pasta, choose the rice since it can be found in nature.

Rule 2. Fewer hands

Looking at the example I just gave you of rice versus pasta, since rice occurs in nature, it means fewer hands touched it or processed it to get it to your table. In an ideal world, you would be able to get it in its most natural state, unbleached or whole-grained. However, pasta has to be created by man. Multiple ingredients have to come together to be prepared and then packaged to get to your table. When faced with this scenario, rice only has to be harvested, then packaged. It can be found in nature in a form you can eat. Use rule two to identify which direction you want your diet to go. Naturally occurring with fewer hands touching means it's less likely to disrupt your digestive system. There is plenty of science that identifies our gut health playing a major role in our overall physical health. In this instance, the fewer hands that touched the food to get to you, the better.

Rule 3. Water is life-giving.

Human beings need water to function. Almost every process that takes place in our bodies, as well as the matter we are made of, is comprised of water. Our blood is comprised of water. Water helps with digestion and transportation of nutrients to our cells. Without water we would die. Drinking water throughout your day will also help with your gut health, physical health, and mental health. Have you ever gotten a headache but don't know why? You are humming along in your day and haven't eaten or drank any fluids. A headache is a sign of dehydration, and your body is notifying you to drink more water. Without looking like a bodybuilder and carrying a jug with you, download an app and track your water consumption. If you don't tick off that you drank a gallon of water for the day, then you need to get to work. Do yourself a favor—drink more water. This is literally the first thing I tell anyone who works with me. Not tea, not coffee, not Gatorade, not PH water—just water.

Rule 4. Balance

Without going into all the various types of diets on the market or trying to help you make sense out of all them, I will simply explain macronutrients (macros) and their consumption. A lot of marketing is done by pitching one diet versus another and demanding you to eat high amounts of one macro versus another. Unfortunately, your body needs all of them: carbohydrates, proteins, and fats. Marketers for each diet will attack one and promote another. There are Pro Carb diets, War on Carb diets, High Fat diets, Protein-only diets. While each may state their case in an effective and conclusive way, there is no getting around that your body requires all three nutrients.

Here is a breakdown of what your daily total caloric consumption should look like:

- Carbohydrates = 40-50% calories consumed. Each gram of carbohydrate yields four calories or energy units per gram.
- Protein = 30-40% calories consumed (1 -2 grams per pound of bodyweight). Each gram of protein yields four calories or energy units per gram.

- Fats = 20-30% calories consumed. Each gram of fat yields nine calories or energy units per gram.

Allow me to give you an example. I am 37-year old male. My physical activity demands require me to eat approximately, 2000-2500 calories (range). This is how many calories I need for my day, considering that I lead a physically active lifestyle and do not sit behind a desk. I weigh approximately 150 pounds (therefore a minimum of 150 grams of protein should be consumed daily).

Simple math → 150 pounds = 150 grams x 4 (calories per gram) = 600 total calories of protein

---

Total of 2000 calories consumed a day = 600 / 2000 = 30%.

Once I have figured out my protein consumption, the other two macros are easier to determine. In this example, because I lead a physically active lifestyle, I should consider eating more than 40% carbohydrates. More energy demands will mean I need more sugars to replenish my depleted energy stores quickly; ergo, I would need to increase the percentage of carbohydrates consumed.

Carbohydrates should always comprise a larger portion of what you consume due to the fact that we basically run on sugar. When looking at percentages, each macro cannot have equal parts of the total caloric allotment. In the smallest form, carbohydrates are broken down into glycogen and then stored for reserve energy. The glycogen molecule is the smallest form of glucose (aka sugar), which runs many of the processes in our bodies. We use glycogen for everything from our brain function to the wiggling of our toes. The other two macronutrients (proteins and fats) also have to be broken down into their smallest units and then converted into glycogen in various processes. So, in this example I chose to allocate 45% of my total calorie consumption to carbohydrates.

Carbs = 45% x 2000 calories = 900/4 calories = 225 grams per day

Fats = 25% x 2000 calories = 500/9 calories = 55.5 grams per day

The final macronutrient breakdown (with my active lifestyle) would look like this:

Carbs = 900 calories or 225 grams per day

Protein = 600calories or 153 grams per day

Fats = 500 calories or 55.5 grams per day

This is merely an example using myself as the subject. As I stated earlier, it should always be a range—40-50% carbohydrates, 30- 40% protein, 20-30% fats—of 2000-2500 calories consumed daily. The reason ranges are necessary is because of stress on the body. Some days stress is greater, whether from mechanical or mental stress, and it causes the body to work overtime. When the body has to perform more work, it requires more energy.

Be careful. There are many advocates for supplements and numerous nutrition gurus out there. Simply know that your body requires all nutrients to work and function optimally. Balance is when you fuel your body according to your needs and lifestyle.

Rule 5: Moderation

Finally, this brings me to Rule 5—moderation. Nowhere in the above nutrition section did I discuss eating outside the scope of the five rules. If you can adhere to these rules 80-85% of the time, you are on your way to a healthier version of yourself. Now that doesn't mean eat five days a week according to these rules, and go nuts on the weekends. Ultimately, that is like spinning your wheels; you will go nowhere fast. It means that if you eat accordingly six days a week and have a night out planned or a meal planned with your loved ones to indulge, go for it! Enjoy that piece of cake or glass of wine; just don't eat the whole cake or drink the whole bottle.

Far too often, I have seen too many people be overly strict with themselves. They try to go from having zero healthy habits to a perfect 100% healthy compliance, only to fail. Eating needs to be a pattern that you can adhere to. Make it simple and fold it seamlessly into your day. Much like the workout plan we have created, choose the number of days you can realistically perform, then add more later as you build up the habits. Like anything else in life, start slowly by creating the habits of eating healthy meals, one meal at a time. This way when you have a treat in the day, you won't feel like you have ruined all your work.

The idea is to teach you how to eat healthy again, creating small victories in your day, and ultimately helping you reach your goals without self-sabotage. Moderation will help you avoid returning to old habits. You know that old way of thinking—being so restrictive until you break and eat a whole pizza and gallon of ice cream? That's the diet monster. If you can follow these above rules I have compiled, you are well on your way to regaining your confidence and slaying the diet monster so you can get on with your journey to a better version of yourself.

I am sorry to have nerded out on you, but there is light at the of end of the tunnel. If you follow these simple rules, you will be able to eat the proper fuel for your lifestyle. To reiterate, follow these five simple rules, and you will be on your way to a healthier version of yourself.

- Stick to naturally occurring foods.
- When you are in doubt about whether or not something seems like a healthier option, ask yourself how many hands touched it to get to the table. Was it made for you or by you? Did it come premade, or was it prepared right before it hit your table? The fewer the number of hands that touched it, the better it is for you.

- Without a doubt, get more water in your diet. It is life-giving and life-sustaining. You cannot live without water, so when in doubt, drink more.
- Rule number four is by far the most complex to follow, but if you understand basics of what macronutrients are, how to identify them, and stick to the ranges, you will be better off long term.

SAMPLE PROGRAM

My Personal Program for Two Bodybuilding & Powerlifting Shows

This is the program I completed for multiple competitions, including two combined bodybuilding and powerlifting meets. This program is the same program I have followed for years and I only modified it to meet the new demands I was going to be under for the dual performance of bodybuilding and powerlifting meets.

<u>Overview of Week:</u>

Mondays: squat

Tuesdays: back

Wednesdays: shoulders

Thursdays: arms

Fridays: squat again

Saturdays: bench

Sundays: recovery or cardio depending on my weight for week.

Day 1 (Monday) First Leg Day
Guidelines:

Sets and reps varied. (4 sets was the minimum allowed)

Back squat: moderate to heavy loads no more than 85% of 1 RM on this day (up to but not exceeding 85%)

Warm-up Movement:

1. Knee extensions, 4 sets 10-20 reps, no rest

2. Anderson squat (squat from the rack up) to warm up, no more than 3-5 reps

Foundational Movements:

1. Back squat, no more than 5-10 reps

2. Leg press or lunges, 15 reps

Cardio and Core:

> 1-mile uphill walk with weighted vest (no more than 20 mins)
>
> Daily morning routine was 500 crunches—not mandatory

Day 2 (Tuesday) Back Attack
Warm-up Movement:

1. Deadlifts, (3-5 sets of partial lifts, for example, from floor to knee to warm up) 3-5 reps

Foundational Movements:

1. Deadlift—full range 5-8 working sets (superset), 1-5 reps

2. Pull-ups weighted, no more than 5 reps (superset)

3. Lats pull down, 10-20 reps

4. Single arm lats-pull down, 10-15 reps

Cardio and Core:

> 1-mile uphill walk with weighted vest (no more than 20 mins)
>
> Daily morning routine was 500 crunches—not mandatory

Day 3 (Wednesday) Shoulder Day
Guidelines: 5-6 sets
Foundational Movements: No supersets

1. Military press, no more than 7 reps

2. Seated Arnold press, 5-10 reps

3. Single arm lateral raise, 10-15 reps

4. Heavy dumbbell lateral raise, 10 reps

Cardio and Core:

    1-mile uphill walk with weighted vest (no more than 20 mins)

    Daily morning routine was 500 crunches—not mandatory

Day 4 (Thursday) Arm Day
Guidelines: 3 supersets, 4 sets each
Foundational Movements: Supersets

1. Barbell curls: 10 reps

Banded triceps kickbacks (extension): 15 reps

1. Dumbbell concentration curls, 10 reps

Incline skull-crushers with EZ-curl bar: 10-15 reps

1. Cable triceps single arm extension, 15 reps

2. Cable rope curls, 15-20 reps.

Cardio and Core:

    1-mile uphill walk with weighted vest (no more than 20 mins)

    Daily morning routine was 500 crunches—not mandatory

Day 5 (Friday) Second Leg Day
Guidelines: 5 sets minimum 1-3 reps
Foundational Movements: (no supersets)

1. Heavy 1/4 squats to rack (negative), 1-2 reps

2. Heavy back squats, no more than 5 reps

3. Split squat or step up, no more than 8 reps

Cardio and Core:

    1-mile uphill walk with weighted vest (no more than 20 mins)

    Daily morning routine was 500 crunches—not mandatory

Day 6 (Saturday) Chest Day

Warm-up Movement:

Dumbbell incline, 4 sets, no more than 10 reps—to force the blood into pectoralis major

Foundational Movement: (no supersets)

1. Flat bench press, 4-6 sets, no more than 5 reps

2. Cable crossover, 3-4 sets, 10 reps

3. Cable fly 3-4 sets 15 reps

Cardio and Core:

    1-mile uphill walk uphill walk with weighted vest (no more than 20 mins)

    Daily morning routine was 500 crunches—not mandatory

Day 7 (Sunday) Rest or Cardio

Cardio and Core:

    30 minutes or stairs or walking with vest on

    Daily morning routine was 500 crunches—not mandatory

MY PROGRAM EXPLANATION

performed the above routine for 18 weeks in preparation for two separate shows. I rarely ever deviated from the above exercise selections; they were my mainstays. Since I was preparing for a powerlifting meet, I tried to stick to the big three movements: the squat, the bench, and the deadlift. The other days were merely for aesthetic purposes for the bodybuilding portion. Traditionally, bodybuilding is about the appearance of symmetry of the body. Most bodybuilders will perform multiple sets and reps of several movements, usually 6 or more exercises. Because I knew that both modalities would take a toll on my system and due to the many injuries I had sustained in my past, I adhered to a "less is more" approach and adapted a limit to the number of exercises I would use to get my body prepared for the dual performance.

The uniqueness of this style of training was I could not allow myself to be so exhausted I could not perform the other modality. If I over-trained my body, I would be way too tired to pose and prepare a bodybuilding routine. Conversely, if I didn't push myself with the weights, I would not have been able to lift in a powerlifting meet. I tried my best to manipulate the variables to help me accommodate this process. Although I did change exercises often, each week I was careful to not change too many pieces of the workout. Often times, I stuck to only the manipulation of the loading structure (see below). I tried to use percentages to help ensure that I gave myself enough stimulus without overdoing it. I stuck to the idea of working three weeks up in percentage and every fourth week dropping to a lower percentage. I set the weeks up to look like the following:

Percentage of Projected Max →	Squat Max (465)	Deadlift Max (500)	Bench Max (275)
70	325	350	192
75	348	375	206
80	372	400	220
85	395	425	233
90	418	450	247
95	440	475	261

Week	Percentage	Reps
One	70-75	8-10
Two	75-80	5-8
Three	85-90	3-5
Four	75-80	4-6
Five	80	5
Six	85	3-5
Seven	90-95	1-3
Eight	70-75	6-8
Nine	75-80	4-8
Ten	85	3-6
Eleven	90-95	1-3
Twelve	70	10
Thirteen	75-80	5-8
Fourteen	85	3-6
Fifteen	90-95	1-3
Sixteen	70	8
Seventeen	75-80	6
Eighteen	85-95	1-3

Note: Week 18 should be close to the last heavy week in preparation for a meet. Week 19 was my taper week, allowing my body time to rest. In other words, I would perform the movements with lighter loads, after the long 18-week build up. In body-building circles this week is called "peak week." This is the week where competitors make final nutritional adjustments, as well, to ensure a dry and lean look specific to the rules of bodybuilding.

However, this process takes a huge toll on your body. I never wanted to make drastic cuts. I did not like the idea of water deprivation, or cutting mass quantities of carbohydrates, virtually depleting my body of essential macronutrients and micronutrients and decreasing my overall energy that could hurt my overall performance. I preferred a longer build up to allow for a more gradual cutting process. For the purposes of the combined bodybuilding and power-lifting meets, I had to maintain my energy levels and wanted to avoid over-stressing my body. My theory behind this was that if I did what I was supposed to do over the previous eighteen weeks, I could now allow my body time to rest during peak week. Of course, I made minor changes to my nutrition to see deeper muscle striations, or more vascularity based on my symmetry, which was determined by how my body looked and felt during posing. I like to spend the final week before I step on stage practicing my posing routine, so it looks more polished, while holding poses for up to two minutes to prepare for any prolonged judging sessions.

MY PERSONAL DIET

My diet for my competition never changed. As I mentioned earlier, the original diet was provided by Lindsay Barkley from Key Potentials, a nutritionist from the west coast. I manipulated it for the competitions, making changes for the needs and demands of the two dual performances. I literally ate the same thing every day for up to 20 weeks. I understand that may not appeal to everyone. I knew what the food was doing for me; it was fueling my performance. I knew the amounts I needed, which made it one less thing for me to worry about. My meals looked like:

MY DIET FOR MY TWO POWERLIFTING
& BODYBUILDING MEETS

Meal 1

6 egg whites with salsa
1 cup of oatmeal with cinnamon and honey
1 tablespoon of peanut butter (usually Smucker's natural brand
with nuts—I prefer chunky style)
1 cup of coffee - black

Meal 2

6 oz chicken, usually a breast
2 slices of whole wheat bread (Killer Dave's brand)

Meal 3

1 cup brown rice
1 cup veggies
1/4 cup of beans
6 oz chicken breast, chopped

Meal 4

Protein shake: 50 g whey chocolate shake made with water
2 rice cakes (one lightly salted, one caramel flavored)

Meal 5

6 oz fish (tilapia)
2 cups of veggies

Drinks (other than coffee)

1 serving pre-workout daily
2 servings of BCAA a day
1 gallon of water a day. I carried a gallon jug and made sure to
finish it every day!

*Cheat meal: If I did cheat at all, I had Mexican food—no cheese and always shrimp with fajita-style vegetables. When my girlfriend took me out for my birthday dinner, that's what we both had. It was the standard cheat meal normally in place of my sixth meal.

CONCLUSION

The ability to share my story with you has been a cathartic experience. My journey has brought forth an inner awareness that there is something inherently wrong within the fitness industry and has exposed my drive to improve the message as the fitness professional I portray to the public. We have been sold far too many ideas and programs depicting what health should be and that somehow it is complex and complicated. We have gotten away from the simplicity of health that centers around movement in our daily lives. There are far too many unnecessary health issues in the world that could be improved if we just moved our bodies.

There are stories all over the internet of body shaming or body dysmorphia. My story began simply with increased movement via sports. Sports opened up a new world for me that helped me create my confidence. I hope my story inspired you to push past your own boundaries and limits to achieve more. My path from sports to coaching was lengthy, but it has led me to developing strategies to help others create confidence for themselves.

The idea of using basic fundamentals may not be new, but it is necessary. I felt compelled to share with the world just how simple creating an effective workout plan can be. The use of the FAB 5, can help you build a sound foundation which will prepare you to conquer any task. Often there is a belief that "more is better," but when it comes to our bodies, "less is more," It is the quality of the questions that must be asked and answered. Each of us needs to have a committed intent to ourselves with the limited time we allocate for our own well-being. That is truly what self-care is about.

You may now proceed forward with the FAB 5 to guide you. Creating a strong foundation will build your confidence to meet life's demands head on. With the introduction of the principles of the FAB 5, you can now go forth and demand a better life because you are armed with the knowledge to do so. No matter your fitness level or the goal you seek, a poor foundation will only make the journey that much harder. I have given you the ability to start again building from the bottom up. Stop jumping from plan to plan, and take the necessary time to fix what is wrong with a focused approach on quality movements.

Some "experts" will tell you that you need to spend all day in the gym. They will explain that more volume will get you bigger and stronger. They will demand you perform countless variations of each type of exercise. They will tell you not to waste time on fundamental movements because they are boring and not attractive. They will have you shy away from work and offer quick answers, like fit-teas or waist trainers. They will tell you about a pill to reduce your waistline.

I have shown you through my example what you can achieve. If you follow the formula of consistency plus work over time, you will be able to accomplish any goal, like that of strength or weight loss. Consistency and effort will bring you the results you demand. You must address your limitations and get back to the basics by focusing on the FAB 5: the squat, the deadlift, the bench press, the overhead press, and the pull-up. These movements are all compound movements that are the pillars for your success. They are basic fundamental movements that will help you create a foundation that will not crumble. The fundamentals are not sexy or exciting, but they work.

A diet is not a list of things you need to avoid. I have given you steadfast rules to help you fix how you view what food is. The food we consume needs to be the fuel for our day. We should embrace natural sources that help make us a weapon against our stressors, to help destroy goals in the gym, and to attack our days with vigor. Andy Frisella, CEO of 1stPhorm, said, "Life is a war: life on earth is a competition. Not a playground—it's a battle ground!"[9].

We must be prepared for anything. We must harden our exterior frames to be capable of dealing with demands we cannot plan for. There is no better way than to become a master of the basics, incorporating each movement into your life, until you have become so proficient at it that you can manipulate your bodyweight in all five directions.

Strength is the ability to move your body through 360 degrees of time and space. Your daily life requires you to be strong for your family, for work, and for your hobbies I have created a plan that helps you achieve that—if you put in the work. Remember that this will not happen overnight. It will take time; you will fail time and time again, but fear not. When it is all said and done, you will become stronger. You will be capable to handle with confidence whatever life has in store for you.

The purpose of this book is to give you the confidence to understand the problematic industry jargon and simplify how to train to accomplish any task. Working out is a necessity for our health. We have become a society that avoids work, looking for instant gratification and quick solutions to our problems. Obesity rates in our youth have skyrocketed due to increased screen time. I grew up in an age where kids ran around in the neighborhood at night until your name was called to come in. We have gotten so far away from movement that our health has become synonymous with pills to fix everything. I can no longer sit idly by, and my solution is to take back your health and confidence through practice of the basics!

TO MY FAMILY

The human body fascinates me. On one hand, it is a labyrinth of nerves, cells, muscles, and fascia, and on the other hand, it's carbon and water. The human body is both complicated and extremely simple to understand. Each day, more scientists, physical therapists, and strength coaches are exploring and understanding more about it. Yet, they still haven't uncovered 100% of what it is capable of. What my body has been able to accomplish after all the injuries and all the time spent in rehabilitation and physical therapy still amazes me.

Unlike my pre-law and criminal justice classes, which never really captivated my soul, the process of me going through rehab after each surgery or trying to work back after minor injuries has literally made me who I am today. I am living proof of what can, cannot, should, and should not be done with your body. If only I was smart enough to catch the signs then to re-adjust and reevaluate what I was doing, perhaps my journey to where I eventually ended up would have been quicker. I am thankful for all I have been through, and as I am writing this and reflecting upon how I got to this moment in time, I can honestly say I wouldn't change it. Quicker would have been much nicer and easier, but as I have gotten older, I have realized something about myself: without struggle or sacrifice, the victories cannot be appreciated. I absolutely loved playing football and loved being competitive. When I was younger, it was about winning; the outcome was important. I still perform daily physical challenges to test my mental capacity to overcome them, but now, it is the journey I have come to love, not the outcome. As I have gotten older, I have become keenly aware that if I do the work every day like I am supposed to, whether I want to or not, the outcome I desire will happen. That is a lesson I can thank both my parents for teaching me.

As I wrote this and I began to ponder more, I don't think I ever recognized before how much my family has helped me along the way. I never gave much thought to my brother giving me the Arnold Schwarzenegger encyclopedia, and I definitely never thanked him. I'm sure I thanked my brother Joe, but I know I never paid him back. I got so caught up and consumed within my own world, I don't think

I recognized just how lousy of a person I was being by not acknowledging them for having my back and helping me out in my time of need. My siblings have definitely supported me throughout my journey to get to the point where I am now, which is why I am writing these words.

My sister Chris has always helped me with small things since I was a kid. She used to help me with my homework and took care of me, watching me when my parents were working. During the summer months when we had a pool, she would pick me up from school and help me with my homework so I could play in the pool. She has since moved and lives in Florida, so wasn't around for a lot of the things happening to me during graduate school. However, she did make the trip to come visit me early in 2019 when our nephew was performing the Sacrament of Communion. She stayed at my place, cleaned up after Joe G., and bought groceries for two men in their thirties. It was cool for her to make the trip and take the time to come to the gym.

Melissa and her husband, Kessar, took care of me and helped me when I broke my foot at the beginning of 2010, letting me stay on their couch and feeding me. Kessar and I spent weekends watching terrible movies for fun. Those are some memories I look back on that make me smile. Melissa came to Ohio in 2015, bringing her two little doggies to stay for three weeks. She was doing a fellowship with Ohio State University at the time, and she too purchased groceries and little odds and ends for the apartment. Joe G. and I are two bachelors living a modest lifestyle with no real frills. We have a con-glomeration of dishware, forks, knives, and spoons, but Melissa took it upon herself to upgrade and get us a set of dishes. She was only visiting, but she tried her hardest to demonstrate a level of care that only a sibling who loves you would.

It is so funny to me to think about these things now, but they are all blessings of coming from such a large family. My family has always watched out for me and I have done a very poor job of returning it in kind. I am sorry I missed those opportunities before to acknowledge all the things they did for me grow-ing up. I previously mentioned how Lisa helped me through graduate school, but words cannot express just how much she has helped me since. She became a saving grace and took the time to make sure I didn't fail miserably. Lisa was my rock and has had my back for a long time. Lisa, Crawford, Antonette and CJ have also opened their home to me since my return to the states, allowing me to live with them indefinitely. So, in these pages, I wish to say to Christina, Melissa, John, Lisa, and Joey—and their families—that I am extremely grateful and proud to be able to call you all my family. I am thankful for each and every one of the things you did in my life to protect me from myself and help me along the way. From the bottom of my heart, thank you! I love each and every one of you.

Finally, I cannot neglect to thank my mother. There are no words for the amount of energy and effort she has given to all of her children. She is an amazing human. She deeply cares and loves us each in her own way. She makes the time to be there for each of us—even when it is not convenient. When I had my foot surgery in 2010, she sat there waiting for me from the moment I went to the hospital to the moment I was released. It was over six hours, but she was there. My mother worked two jobs while we were growing up. I am not sure how I can ever repay her, but I hope these words begin the process. Mom, I love you more every day as I get older. I cannot imagine doing the things you did for us growing up and the things you continue to do. I will always be grateful for the life you have provided me and pray that you know just how thankful I am to call you mother. Louise Cosenza is one of the most caring, loving people you will ever meet. I hope she knows that everything I've done in my life is to make her and my father proud.

Mom, may you live the rest of your days surrounded by the love of your children and grand-children. I love you and I truly appreciate everything you have done for me!

To my father, John A. Cosenza, I hope I make you proud of the man I have become.

Thank you; Joe, Lisa, John, Melissa, Christina, & Louise Cosenza!

ACKNOWLEDGMENTS

Outside my family, there are a handful of people I would especially like to thank for being with me and helping me evolve in some way.

A special thank you to Keith Harney for the photographs. Keith's skill is truly amazing he was able the exact movements and exercises to highlight the prime movers of the exercises. He was also able to make me look good in the process; much appreciated thank you brother!

To my former business partner, Joe Gernetzke: without you, I wouldn't have been able to leave Columbus to pursue my education in strength and conditioning further, which ultimately gave me the time to write this book. You are a good friend. Thank you!

To my best friend growing up, Mathew Delpriore: you believed in me at the beginning of my venture to start Sentinel Performance, LLC. You continue to be a true confidante and great friend. I look forward to the many years we have left creating more and more memories. We have known one another since we were 12 years old. I pray you and your family are always safe, healthy, and happy. I look forward to watching our children play together and the countless family barbeques to come!

Last but, not least, I would like to take a moment to appreciate and thank my "editor-in-chief" and friend, Dionne Vernon, DPT. Although we have not known each other for very long, our paths crossed at the right time. We were both working to better our lives when we met, and we were able to assist each other in moments of great trepidation. It is not often you meet someone who is on such an upswing in their life, and I look forward to watching just how far you soar! I will always be indebted to you for your help with the writing of this book, as well as innumerable moments when you were able to help me refocus my perspective during our time working together. From the bottom of my heart, I am thankful for our time spent working together, getting to know one another, and your friendship. I am not sure I would have survived without you. Words cannot do justice for the gratitude in my heart. Once again, thank you.

CLIENT TESTIMONIALS

I have known Frank for about 6 years, but never had a chance to work with him until recently. While training in martial arts, I suffered a partial tear in my MCL. Thankfully, my tear did not require surgery, but the rehab instructions were minimal at best. That's when I reached out to Frank. After a thorough discussion of the injury and my physical limitations, he put together a plan to do virtual (FaceTime) physical therapy sessions. I appreciated him sharing his knowledge and explaining to me how each exercise activates a muscle group that ultimately benefits the injured area. The virtual training sessions were efficient and convenient, I felt like I was working with one of the best trainers in the country that otherwise I wouldn't have access to. I was so impressed with the breadth of his knowledge and the results I began to see in my recovery that I asked him to put together a nutrition and supplement plan. Combining training with a nutritional game plan is a potent combination very few trainers address let alone have a functional knowledge in. Having a holistic approach coordinated by Frank has proven to be a key component in my speedy recovery. ~Laith Khalaf

I have worked with Frank for approximately 2 years. During this time, I have been focusing on getting both leaner and stronger, and I have had little to no reservations that he was helping me work toward my goals. If there was one thing that I would do over again related to my fitness goals and lifestyle, it would have been that I would want the opportunity to meet Frank much earlier in my quest. I am 46 years old now and truly believe that not only my body, but my mind and soul would have had the benefit for feeling the way that I do today. I feel he assisted me in creating superior discipline to achieve more out of life. I am extremely thankful I found him, and I would wholeheartedly recommend him to everyone who needs fitness training. ~Todd Bullock

I worked with Frank for almost a year but continue to call on him for his expertise when needed. During the time I was training with him, I simply wanted to get back in to shape and push myself a little harder. Frank was just the person I needed, and I had little to no reservations that he was helping me work toward my goal. I feel he assisted me in gaining confidence for myself that has shaped the discipline I now have to achieve more out of life and in the gym. I am extremely thankful I found him, and I would wholeheartedly recommend him to everyone who needs fitness training. ~Amy Riggenbach

I have worked with Frank since March of 2018. During this time, I have lifted in three full powerlifting meets and one bench meet. Being a female in this industry can feel a little uncomfortable, but Frank made me feel empowered and motivated to keep pushing my body. Through that time Frank has taught me about how my diet influences my lifts and body composition. He has taught me to have a better relationship with food and not to punish myself if I get a little off track. I feel he assisted me in creating the confidence I need to achieve more out of life. I am extremely thankful I reached out to him, and I would highly recommend him to everyone who needs fitness and nutrition training. ~Sheila Hahn

ENDNOTES

1   Parisi, Bill, and Johnathon Allen. *Fascia Training: A Whole-System Approach*. Parisi Media Productions, 2019.

2   Ferriss, Timothy. *Tools of Titans: The Tactics, Routines, and Habits of Billionaires, Icons, and World-Class Performers*. New York, NY: Houghton Mifflin Harcourt, 2016.

3   Ferriss, Timothy. *Tools of Titans: The Tactics, Routines, and Habits of Billionaires, Icons, and World-Class Performers*. New York, NY: Houghton Mifflin Harcourt, 2016.

4   Photo adapted from Muscle in Motion

5   Photo adapted from Muscle in Motion

6   Photo adapted from google search "bar path"

7   Photo adapted from Muscle and Motion

8   Tinsley, Grant. "Cardio vs. Weightlifting: Which Is Better for Weight Loss?" Healthline.com. Heathline Media, October 24, 2017. https://www.healthline.com/nutrition/cardio-vs-weights-for-weight-loss.

9   Do You Feel Alone? Andy Frisella, Podcast MFCEO, ep 297 April 11, 2019

Made in the USA
Columbia, SC
13 September 2021